IMPACT

CALIFORNIA SOCIAL STUDIES

U.S. History

Making a New Nation

INQUIRY JOURNAL

McGraw-Hill Education

Mc
Graw
Hill

Program Authors

James Banks, Ph.D.
Kerry and Linda Killinger Endowed Chair in Diversity Studies
Director, Center for Multicultural Education
University of Washington
Seattle, Washington

Kevin P. Colleary, Ed.D.
Curriculum and Teaching Department
Graduate School of Education
Fordham University
New York, New York

William Deverell, Ph.D.
Director of the Huntington-USC Institute on California and the West
Professor of History, University of Southern California
Los Angeles, California

Daniel Lewis, Ph.D.
Dibner Senior Curator
The Huntington Library
Los Angeles, California

Elizabeth Logan Ph.D., J.D.
Associate Director of the Huntington-USC Institute on California and the West
Los Angeles, California

Walter C. Parker, Ph.D.
Professor of Social Studies Education
Adjunct Professor of Political Science
University of Washington
Seattle, Washington

Emily M. Schell, Ed.D.
Professor, Teacher Education
San Diego State University
San Diego, California

mheducation.com/prek-12

Send all inquiries to:
McGraw-Hill Education
120 S. Riverside Plaza, Suite 1200
Chicago, IL 60606

ISBN: 978-0-07-899365-7
MHID: 0-07-899365-2

Printed in the United States of America.

6 7 8 9 10 LWI 23 22 21 20

Program Consultants

Jana Echevarria, Ph.D.
Professor Emerita
California State University
Long Beach, California

Douglas Fisher, Ph.D.
Professor, Educational Leadership
San Diego State University
San Diego, California

Carlos Ulloa, Ed.D.
Principal, Escondido Union School District
Escondido, California

Rebecca Valbuena, M.Ed.
K-5 Teacher on Special Assignment/Academic Coach
Glendora Unified School District
Glendora, California

Program Reviewers

Gary Clayton, Ph.D.
Professor of Economics
Northern Kentucky University
Highland Heights, Kentucky

Lorri Glover, Ph.D.
John Francis Bannon, S.J. Professor of History
Saint Louis University
St. Louis, Missouri

Thomas Herman, Ph.D.
Project Director, Center for Interdisciplinary Studies of Youth and Space
Department of Geography
San Diego State University

Nafees Khan, Ph.D.
Department of Teaching and Learning
Social Studies Education
Clemson University
Clemson, South Carolina

Clifford Trafzer, Ph.D.
Distinguished Professor of History
Rupert Costo Chair in American Indian Affairs
University of California
Riverside, California

Letter from the Authors

Dear Social Studies Detective,

Think about the United States of America. Why did different groups of people decide to settle in the territory that would become the United States? When those regions came together, how did the economy, the politics, and groups of people change? In this book, you will find out more about how a territory became a nation. You will think about what it meant to become an independent United States—and what it means to be an American.

As you read, take on the role of a detective. As questions come to your mind, write them down. Then analyze the text to find the answers. What piques your interest? Take notes as you read. You will use your notes as you share what you learned with your classmates. Look closely at all the text—photos, maps, timelines, and historical documents will bring the history of the United States to life!

Enjoy your investigation into the world of social studies where you will explore how a group of territories became the United States, a place full of women, men, and children who came from many places to form a growing and diverse country!

Sincerely,

The IMPACT Social Studies Authors

PRIMARY SOURCE

IN CONGRESS, JULY 4, 1776.

The unanimous Declaration of the thirteen united States of America,

Declaration of Independence

Contents

Reference Sources

Chapter 1

The Land and People Before Columbus

Where and How Did American Indians Live Before the Arrival of Europeans?

The Age of Exploration

What Happened When Diverse Cultures Crossed Paths?

A Changing Continent

How Did European Settlements Impact North America?

The Road to War

Why Would a Nation Want to Become Independent?

Chapter 5

The American Revolution

What Does the Revolutionary Era Tell Us About Our Nation Today?

Chapter 6

Forming a New Government

How Does the Constitution Help Us Understand What It Means to Be an American?

Life in the Young Republic

How Were the Early Years of the United States Transformative for the Nation?

Chapter 8

The Westward Expansion

What Does the Westward Expansion Reveal About the Character of Our Nation?

Skills and Features

Inquiry and Analysis Skills

Reader's Theater

My Notes

Getting Started

You have two social studies books that you will use together to explore and analyze important Social Studies issues.

The Inquiry Journal is your reporter's notebook where you will ask questions, analyze sources, and record information.

The Research Companion is where you'll read nonfiction and literature selections, examine primary source materials, and look for answers to your questions.

Every Chapter

Chapter opener pages help you see the big picture. Each chapter begins with an **Essential Question**. This **EQ** guides research and inquiry.

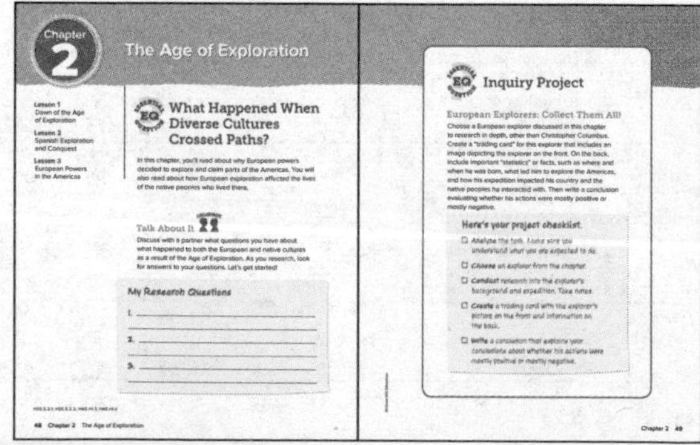

In the **Inquiry Journal,** you'll talk about the **EQ** and find out about the EQ Inquiry Project for the chapter.

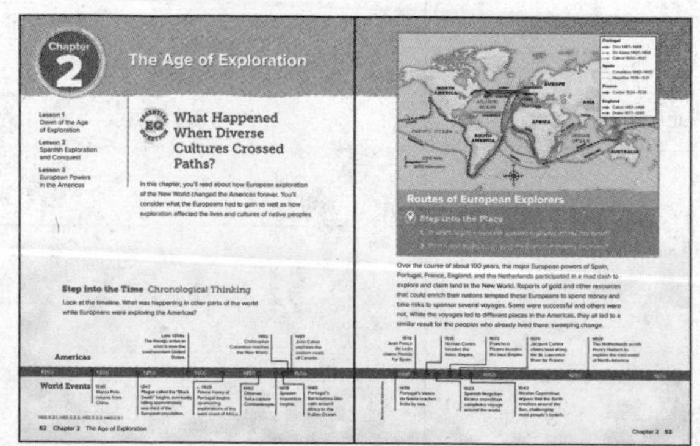

In the **Research Companion**, you'll explore the **EQ** and use a time line and map to establish the lesson's time and place.

StasKhom/iStock/Getty Images

Explore Words

Find out what you know about the chapter's academic vocabulary.

Explore Words

Complete this chapter's Word Rater. Write notes as you learn more about each word.

charter — My Notes
- ☐ Know It!
- ☐ Heard It!
- ☐ Don't Know It!

claim — My Notes
- ☐ Know It!
- ☐ Heard It!
- ☐ Don't Know It!

colony — My Notes
- ☐ Know It!
- ☐ Heard It!
- ☐ Don't Know It!

conquest — My Notes
- ☐ Know It!
- ☐ Heard It!
- ☐ Don't Know It!

diverse — My Notes
- ☐ Know It!
- ☐ Heard It!
- ☐ Don't Know It!

merchants — My Notes
- ☐ Know It!
- ☐ Heard It!
- ☐ Don't Know It!

navigation — My Notes
- ☐ Know It!
- ☐ Heard It!
- ☐ Don't Know It!

resistance — My Notes
- ☐ Know It!
- ☐ Heard It!
- ☐ Don't Know It!

settlement — My Notes
- ☐ Know It!
- ☐ Heard It!
- ☐ Don't Know It!

warship — My Notes
- ☐ Know It!
- ☐ Heard It!
- ☐ Don't Know It!

50 Chapter 2 The Age of Exploration

Chapter 2 51

Connect Through Literature

Cabin Boy Aboard the Buena Estrella

From the Journal of Dominic Raimundo, Age 10

by Jennifer Buchet
Illustrated by Shelley Jackson

What if you could have sailed with an explorer 400 years ago? This is what your days might have been like.

August 5, 1524 At last, the winds are with us. I'm anxious to reach New Spain[1] and discover my fortune! Every day, I rise at 3 a.m. to wake the crew. I sing the morning hymns. Cook and I then lay out salted pork and ale for everyone. Afterward, I help the captain with the logbooks that record everything that is happening. And then I walk the ship, working wherever I'm needed. Yesterday, I helped stop up a small leak. I still smell the awful odor of tar on me. Perhaps tomorrow, I can bathe with a bucket of seawater.

August 15 I miss my bed at home! I didn't have enough money to buy a hammock before we left Spain. So I sleep against sacks of grain or with the horses. But it really smells down below! ... are clear, I sleep topside and stargaze. The clanging of the rigging (the ropes and metal fixtures) and the whoosh of the waves are my lullaby.

August 22 The sky has been darkening all day. The air is heavy. Captain Padilla ordered us to batten down the hatches (to cover up the entrances to go below deck) and secure all the lines. Even the dolphins have gone. I'm afraid . . .

[1]In the 1500s, Spain had claimed a huge area of land in North America. The land was called New Spain.

August 26 Dios mío, I'm alive! These last few days have been the worst of my life. I feared a giant sea monster was trying to devour us all! I couldn't tell if it was day or night, so dark was the sky. The ship bucked and pitched in the merciless waves. Twice we nearly capsized! Sadly, three sailors fell into the churning seas. Water was everywhere, including below deck. I helped pump the bilge, trying to ignore the horses' terrified cries. My arms still ache, but at least I'm alive.

August 28 We limp toward Havana for repairs. Captain Padilla says our expedition is delayed by at least three weeks! Food supplies are low and tempers are high. We couldn't collect rainwater during the storm, and now our barrels are filled with algae scum. The remaining cheese is moldy, and sometimes it hurts to bite into what's left of the hardtack. Hard is the right word for those biscuits! I remind myself that gold and glory await me.

September 8 At last, dry land! Some sailors talk of staying in Cuba, finding work in the gold mines or on the sugarcane farms. But I'll continue; after that hurricane, I don't even fear the Indians![2]

[2]Because Columbus thought he had reached the Indies in Asia, he called the people of the Caribbean "Indians." Later explorers used the same name.

Think About It

1. What motivated Dominic travel to the New Spain?
2. How would you describe the journey from Spain to New Spain?
3. Think about Dominic's character. What characteristics does he show that are necessary for survival in the journey to the New World?

54 Chapter 2 The Age of Exploration

Chapter 2 55

Connect Through Literature

Explore the chapter topic through fiction, informational text, and poetry.

People You Should Know

Learn about the lives of people who have made an impact in history.

People You Should Know

Moctezuma II

At the time of the arrival of Spanish conquistador Hernan Cortés, Moctezuma II controlled the Aztec empire. Moctezuma, however, often demanded sacrifices from tribes that were his subjects. Years of these demands had led many people to dislike him. When Cortés kidnapped Moctezuma, Cortés assumed the Aztecs would not fight for fear of endangering their ruler. The people were only too glad to be rid of Moctezuma, however, and the fight that followed resulted in Moctezuma's death.

Marco Polo

The Italian merchant Marco Polo was one of the world's first travel writers. He, his father, and his uncle traveled from Europe across the Middle East, India, China, Vietnam, and back again. Polo told of his 24 years of adventures in a classic piece of literature called *Il Milione*, or *The Million*. This title probably comes from Polo's nickname, which referred to his tendency to talk about the millions of things he had seen.

Queen Isabella I of Spain

Born a princess of Castile, Isabella united all of Spain when she married Ferdinand I of Aragon. Together, they conquered Grenada and increased the size of their empire. It was as she was encamped with her army at Grenada that an Italian explorer named Christopher Columbus approached her. He asked for her support for an expedition to find a western route to Asia. She agreed to give him some money, seeing an opportunity to enrich her country.

Atahualpa

After the death of his father, Inca emperor Huayna Capac, Atahualpa waged a war with his half-brother for the Inca throne. Only a few months after his victory, however, Atahualpa's reign was cut short. Spanish conquistador Francisco Pizarro entered the Inca city of Cuzco in November of 1532. Pizarro invited Atahualpa to a feast. Using the example set by Hernan Cortés, Pizarro captured Atahualpa and killed his soldiers. The Inca emperor promised the Spaniard mountains of gold and silver in return for his release. Once the riches had been delivered, however, Pizarro killed Atahualpa anyway and ended the Inca empire.

56 Chapter 2 The Age of Exploration

Chapter 2 57

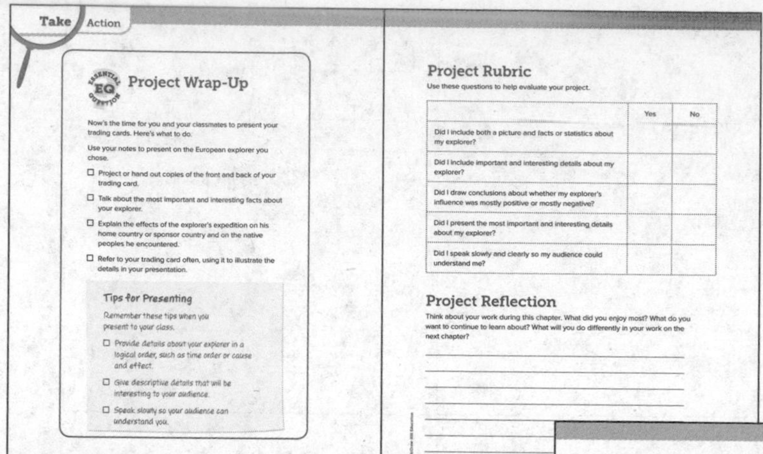

Take Action

Project Wrap-Up

Now's the time for you and your classmates to present your trading cards. Here's what to do.

Use your notes to present on the European explorer you chose.

- ☐ Project or hand out copies of the front and back of your trading card.
- ☐ Talk about the most important and interesting facts about your explorer.
- ☐ Explain the effects of the explorer's expedition on his home country or sponsor country and on the native peoples he encountered.
- ☐ Refer to your trading card often, using it to illustrate the details in your presentation.

Tips for Presenting

Remember these tips when you present to your class.

- ☐ Provide details about your explorer in a logical order, such as time order or cause and effect.
- ☐ Give descriptive details that will be interesting to your audience.
- ☐ Speak slowly so your audience can understand you.

76 Chapter 2 The Age of Exploration

Project Rubric

Use these questions to help evaluate your project.

	Yes	No
Did I include both a picture and facts or statistics about my explorer?		
Did I include important and interesting details about my explorer?		
Did I draw conclusions about whether my explorer's influence was mostly positive or mostly negative?		
Did I present the most important and interesting details about my explorer?		
Did I speak slowly and clearly so my audience could understand me?		

Project Reflection

Think about your work during this chapter. What did you enjoy most? What do you want to continue to learn about? What will you do differently in your work on the next chapter?

Take Action

Present your Inquiry project to your class and assess your work with the project rubric. Then take time to reflect on your work.

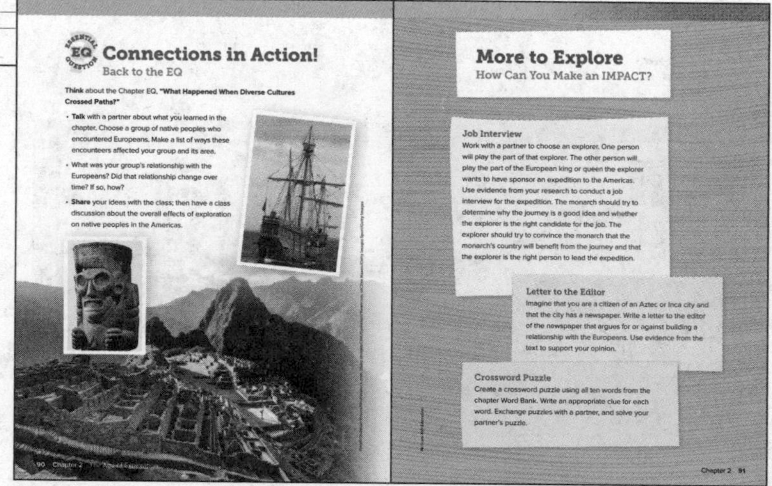

Connections in Action!

Back to the EQ

Think about the Chapter EQ, **"What Happened When Diverse Cultures Crossed Paths?"**

- **Talk** with a partner about what you learned in the chapter. Choose a group of native peoples who encountered Europeans. Make a list of ways these encounteers affected your group and its area.
- What was your group's relationship with the Europeans? Did that relationship change over time? If so, how?
- **Share** your ideas with the class; then have a class discussion about the overall effects of exploration on native peoples in the Americas.

More to Explore

How Can You Make an IMPACT?

Job Interview

Work with a partner to choose an explorer. One person will play the part of that explorer. The other person will play the part of the European king or queen the explorer wants to have sponsor an expedition to the Americas. Use evidence from your research to conduct a job interview for the expedition. The monarch should try to determine why the journey is a good idea and whether the explorer is the right candidate for the job. The explorer should try to convince the monarch that the monarch's country will benefit from the journey and that the explorer is the right person to lead the expedition.

Letter to the Editor

Imagine that you are a citizen of an Aztec or Inca city and that the city has a newspaper. Write a letter to the editor of the newspaper that argues for or against building a relationship with the Europeans. Use evidence from the text to support your opinion.

Crossword Puzzle

Create a crossword puzzle using all ten words from the chapter Word Bank. Write an appropriate clue for each word. Exchange puzzles with a partner, and solve your partner's puzzle.

Chapter 2 91

Connections in Action

Think about the people, places, and events you read about in the chapter. Discuss with a partner how this gives you a deeper understanding of the EQ.

Every Lesson

Lesson 2

How Did Spanish Exploration Change the Lives of People in the Americas?

Lesson Outcomes

What Am I Learning?

In this lesson, you're going to use your investigative skills to learn how Spanish contact and exploration in the Americas changed the lives of the native peoples living there.

Why Am I Learning It?

Reading and talking about the effects of Spanish contact and exploration will help you understand changes that took place and that helped shape the Americas in the future.

How Will I Know That I Learned It?

You will be able to identify the causes and explain the effects of the Columbian Exchange and of Spanish conquest, exploration, and colonization of the Americas.

Talk About It

COLLABORATE

Look at the Details Examine the image of Cortés and his men. Based on this painting, do you predict their interactions with native peoples will end peacefully or violently?

HSS.5.2.1, HSS.5.2.2, HSS.5.2.3, HSS.5.3.1, HAS.CS.1, HAS.CS.2, HAS.CS.3, HAS.CS.4, HAS.CS.5, HAS.HR.1, HAS.HR.2, HAS.HI.1, HAS.HI.3, HAS.HI.4

60 Lesson 2 How Did Spanish Exploration Change the Lives of People in the Americas?

Hernan Cortés at Vera Cruz in 1519, where he decided to found a village.

Lesson Question lets you think about how the lesson connects to the chapter EQ.

Lesson Outcomes help you to think about what you will be learning and how it applies to the EQ.

Images and text provide opportunities to explore the lesson topic.

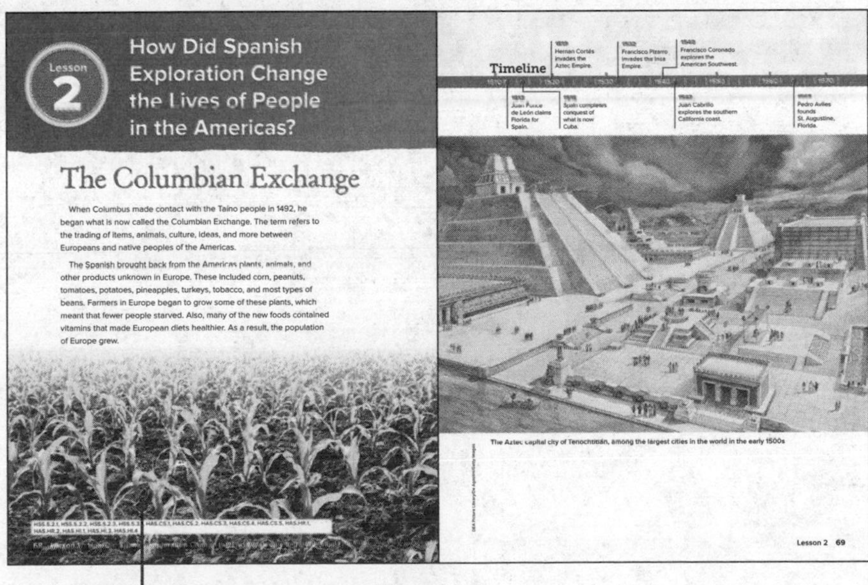

Lesson 2

How Did Spanish Exploration Change the Lives of People in the Americas?

The Columbian Exchange

When Columbus made contact with the Taino people in 1492, he began what is now called the Columbian Exchange. The term refers to the trading of items, animals, culture, ideas, and more between Europeans and native peoples of the Americas.

The Spanish brought back from the Americas plants, animals, and other products unknown in Europe. These included corn, peanuts, tomatoes, potatoes, pineapples, turkeys, tobacco, and most types of beans. Farmers in Europe began to grow some of these plants, which meant that fewer people starved. Also, many of the new foods contained vitamins that made European diets healthier. As a result, the population of Europe grew.

The Aztec capital city of Tenochtitlán, among the largest cities in the world in the early 1500s

Lesson 2 69

Lesson selections deepen your understanding of the lesson topic and its connection to the EQ.

Analyze and Inquire

The Inquiry Journal provides the tools you need to analyze a source. You'll use those tools to investigate the texts in the Research Companion and use the graphic organizer in the Inquiry Journal to organize your findings.

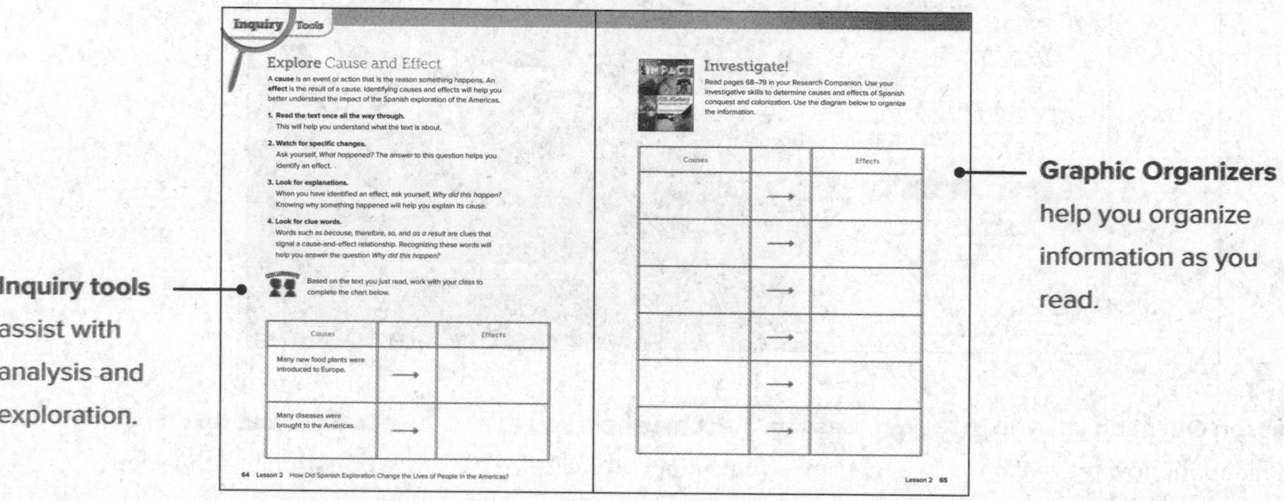

Inquiry Tools

Explore Cause and Effect

A **cause** is an event or action that is the reason something happens. An **effect** is the result of a cause. Identifying causes and effects will help you better understand the impact of the Spanish exploration of the Americas.

1. **Read the text once all the way through.**
   This will help you understand what the text is about.
2. **Watch for specific changes.**
   Ask yourself, *What happened?* The answer to this question helps you identify an effect. .
3. **Look for explanations.**
   When you have identified an effect, ask yourself, *Why did this happen?* Knowing why something happened will help you explain its cause.
4. **Look for clue words.**
   Words such as *because, therefore, so,* and *as a result* are clues that signal a cause-and-effect relationship. Recognizing these words will help you answer the question *Why did this happen?*

COLLABORATE Based on the text you just read, work with your class to complete the chart below.

Causes		Effects
Many new food plants were introduced to Europe.	→	
Many diseases were brought to the Americas.	→	

64 Lesson 2 How Did Spanish Exploration Change the Lives of People in the Americas?

Investigate!

Read pages 68–79 in your Research Companion. Use your investigative skills to determine causes and effects of Spanish conquest and colonization. Use the diagram below to organize the information.

Causes		Effects
	→	
	→	
	→	
	→	
	→	
	→	

Lesson 2 65

Inquiry tools assist with analysis and exploration.

Graphic Organizers help you organize information as you read.

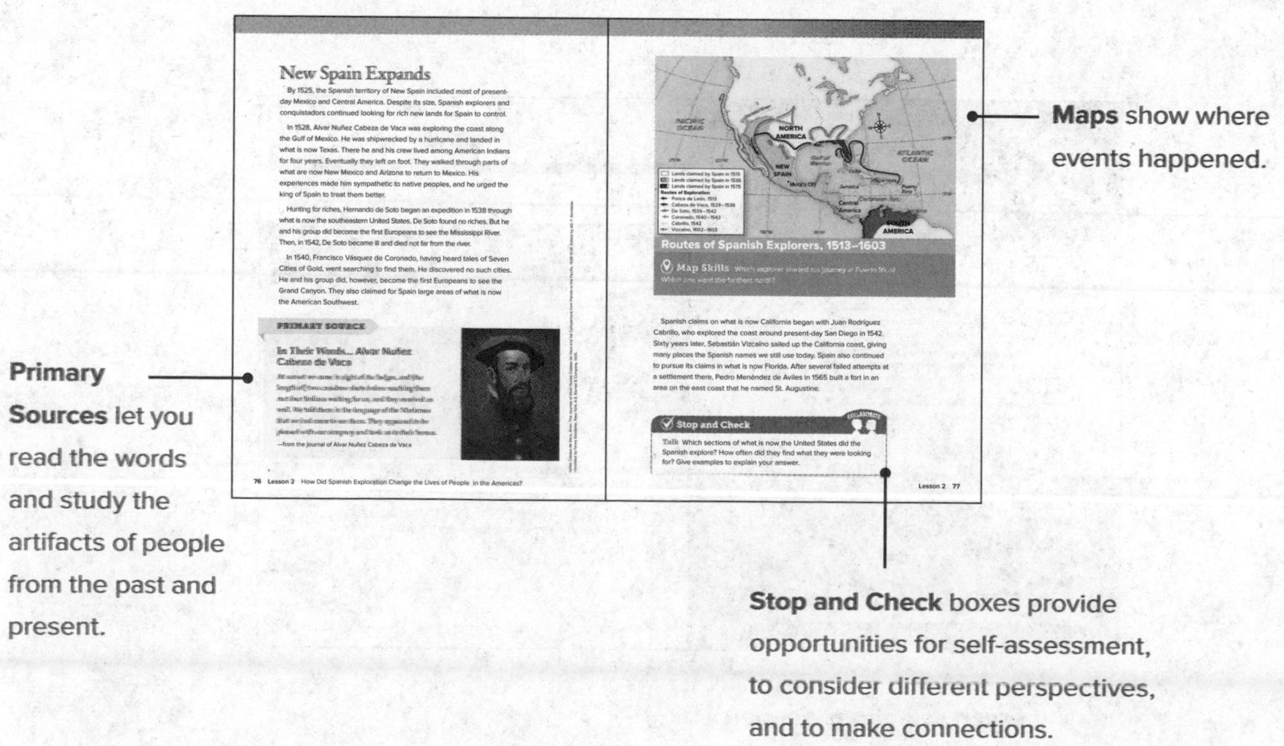

New Spain Expands

By 1525, the Spanish territory of New Spain included most of present-day Mexico and Central America. Despite its size, Spanish explorers and conquistadors continued looking for rich new lands for Spain to control.

In 1528, Alvar Nuñez Cabeza de Vaca was exploring the coast along the Gulf of Mexico. He was shipwrecked by a hurricane and landed in what is now Texas. There he and his crew lived among American Indians for four years. Eventually they left on foot. They walked through parts of what are now New Mexico and Arizona to return to Mexico. His experiences made him sympathetic to native peoples, and he urged the king of Spain to treat them better.

Hunting for riches, Hernando de Soto began an expedition in 1538 through what is now the southeastern United States. De Soto found no riches. But he and his group did become the first Europeans to see the Mississippi River. Then, in 1542, De Soto became ill and died not far from the river.

In 1540, Francisco Vásquez de Coronado, having heard tales of Seven Cities of Gold, went searching to find them. He discovered no such cities. He and his group did, however, become the first Europeans to see the Grand Canyon. They also claimed for Spain large areas of what is now the American Southwest.

PRIMARY SOURCE

In Their Words... Alvar Nuñez Cabeza de Vaca

—from the journal of Alvar Nuñez Cabeza de Vaca

76 Lesson 2 How Did Spanish Exploration Change the Lives of People in the Americas?

Routes of Spanish Explorers, 1513–1603

Map Skills

Spanish claims on what is now California began with Juan Rodríguez Cabrillo, who explored the coast around present-day San Diego in 1542. Sixty years later, Sebastián Vizcaíno sailed up the California coast, giving many places the Spanish names we still use today. Spain also continued to pursue its claims in what is now Florida. After several failed attempts at a settlement there, Pedro Menéndez de Aviles in 1565 built a fort in an area on the east coast that he named St. Augustine.

Stop and Check

COLLABORATE

Talk Which sections of what is now the United States did the Spanish explore? How often did they find what they were looking for? Give examples to explain your answer.

Lesson 2 77

Maps show where events happened.

Primary Sources let you read the words and study the artifacts of people from the past and present.

Stop and Check boxes provide opportunities for self-assessment, to consider different perspectives, and to make connections.

Report Your Findings

At the end of each lesson you have an opportunity in the Inquiry Journal to report your findings and connect back to the EQ. In the Research Companion, you'll reconsider the lesson focus question based on what you've learned.

Think about what you have learned.

Write about it using text evidence to support your ideas.

Connect to the EQ.

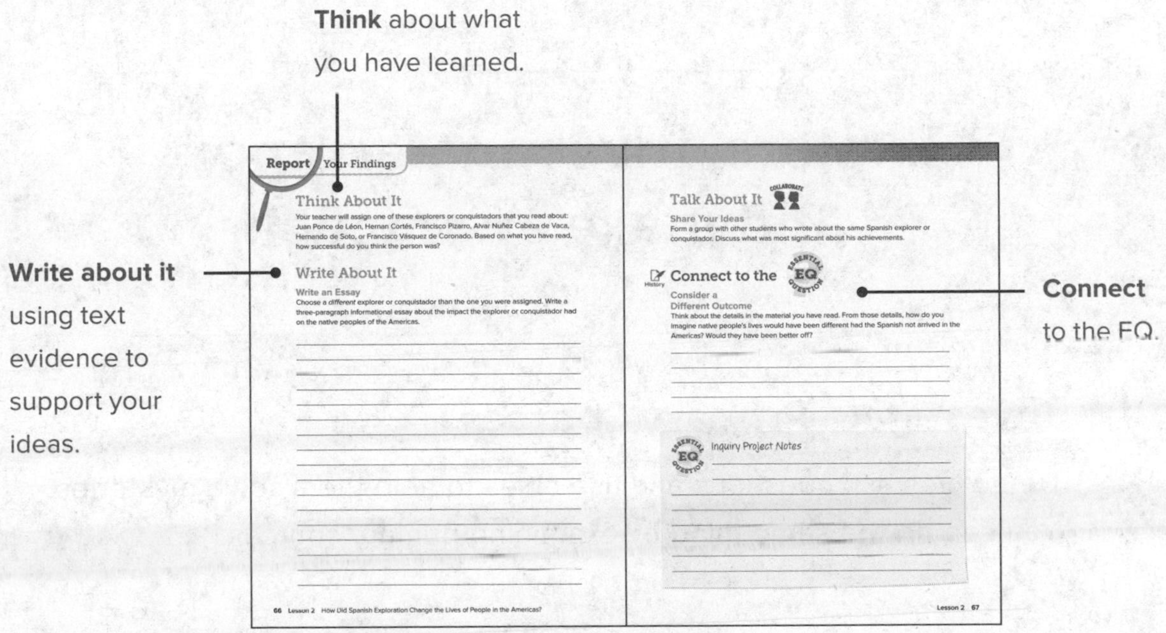

Report Your Findings

Think About It

Your teacher will assign one of these explorers or conquistadors that you read about: Juan Ponce de Léon, Hernan Cortés, Francisco Pizarro, Alvar Nuñez Cabeza de Vaca, Hernando de Soto, or Francisco Vásquez de Coronado. Based on what you have read, how successful do you think the person was?

Write About It

Write an Essay

Choose a *different* explorer or conquistador than the one you were assigned. Write a three-paragraph informational essay about the impact the explorer or conquistador had on the native peoples of the Americas.

66 Lesson 2 How Did Spanish Exploration Change the Lives of People in the Americas?

Talk About It

Share Your Ideas

Form a group with other students who wrote about the same Spanish explorer or conquistador. Discuss what was most significant about his achievements.

Connect to the EQ

Consider a Different Outcome

Think about the details in the material you have read. From those details, how do you imagine native people's lives would have been different had the Spanish not arrived in the Americas? Would they have been better off?

Inquiry Project Notes

Lesson 2 67

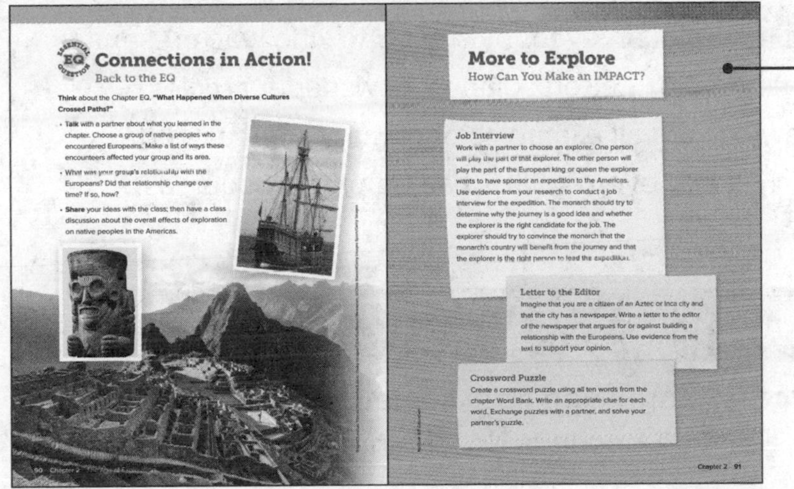

Connections in Action!

Back to the EQ

Think about the Chapter EQ, **"What Happened When Diverse Cultures Crossed Paths?"**

- **Talk** with a partner about what you learned in the chapter. Choose a group of native peoples who encountered Europeans. Make a list of ways these encounteers affected your group and its area.
- What was your group's relationship with the Europeans? Did that relationship change over time? If so, how?
- **Share** your ideas with the class; then have a class discussion about the overall effects of exploration on native peoples in the Americas.

More to Explore

How Can You Make an IMPACT?

Job Interview

Work with a partner to choose an explorer. One person will play the part of that explorer. The other person will play the part of the European king or queen the explorer wants to have sponsor an expedition to the Americas. Use evidence from your research to conduct a job interview for the expedition. The monarch should try to determine why the journey is a good idea and whether the explorer is the right candidate for the job. The explorer should try to convince the monarch that the monarch's country will benefit from the journey and that the explorer is the right person to lead the expedition.

Letter to the Editor

Imagine that you are a citizen of an Aztec or Inca city and that the city has a newspaper. Write a letter to the editor of the newspaper that argues for or against building a relationship with the Europeans. Use evidence from the text to support your opinion.

Crossword Puzzle

Create a crossword puzzle using all ten words from the chapter Word Bank. Write an appropriate clue for each word. Exchange puzzles with a partner, and solve your partner's puzzle.

Chapter 2 91

Think about what you read in the lesson. How does this give you a new understanding about the lesson focus question?

Be a Social Studies Detective

How do you learn about people, places, and events in the present or in the past and the impact they had on history? Become a Social Studies Detective!

Explore, investigate, report, and make an impact!

Investigate Primary Sources

Detectives ask questions and use clues to help them solve mysteries. You can do the same thing by examining primary sources.

What's a Primary Source?

A **primary source** is a record of an event by someone who was present at the event when it happened. Letters, diaries, newspaper articles, photographs, and drawings are all examples of primary sources. Birth certificates, bank records, and even clothes can be primary sources.

Did You Know?

A **secondary source** is information from someone who was not present at the event he or she is describing. Secondary sources are based on primary sources.

StasKhom/iStock/Getty Images

PRIMARY SOURCE

Social Studies Detective Strategies

Inspect

- Look closely at the source.
- Who or what is it?
- How would you describe it?

Find Evidence

- Where did the event take place?
- When did it happen?
- What are the most important details?

Make Connections

- Is this source like others you found?
- Are there other perspectives that you need to consider?
- What information supports your idea?

Social Studies Detectives examine primary sources to make connections. These connections help them learn about the past and understand the present. Use the Social Studies Detective Strategy to analyze the image below.

PRIMARY SOURCE

Social Studies Detective Strategies

1. Inspect
2. Find Evidence
3. Make Connections

Inspect the primary source below. Ask questions. Who wrote the diary? When did they write it? Why do you think they wrote it? Look for clues to answer your questions.

June 3d, Sunday. We left El Paso at eight this morning, and rode until ten, when we reached a deserted rancho, and with some trouble encamped near a river bed with waterholes along it. A beautiful lagoon with water holes a hundred yards long enabled us all to take refreshing baths, and I watched with pleasure the languid flight of the great blue heron, changing his position as he was approached. Two Mexicans, hunting cattle, came to us here, and Lieut. Browning bought a wild mule, for which he gave a few dollars and a broken down mule. (p.94)

September 2d. Two days out from Ures we came to some Pimos Indians washing gold from black ore, which they said produced well; we found some lumps of ore in the dust, all of irregular shapes. The value is only about one real (about ten cents) for each bushel of dirt. Each man made about two dollars a day.
We had fine grass and pond water here, and are off for Altar. (P.143)

from *Audubon's Western Journal: 1849-1850*

TEXT: Audubon, John W. Audubon's Western Journal: 1849-1850. Cleveland: The Arthur H. Clark Company, 1906.; PHOTO: McGraw-Hill Education

Explore Geography

Geographers are detectives who understand how our world is connected by studying the earth's surface and digging for clues about how people have shaped our planet. This section gives you the tools that you'll need as you explore geography.

StasKhom/iStock/Getty Images

Reading a Map

Maps are drawings of places on Earth. Most maps have standard features to help you read the map.

Map Title The map title tells you what information is on the map.

Inset Map An inset map is a small map included on a larger map. The inset map might show an area that is too large, too small, or too far away to be included on the main map.

Boundary Lines Boundary lines are political. The boundaries between states usually are drawn differently from the boundaries between nations.

Locator A locator map is a small map set into the main map. It shows the area of the map in a larger region.

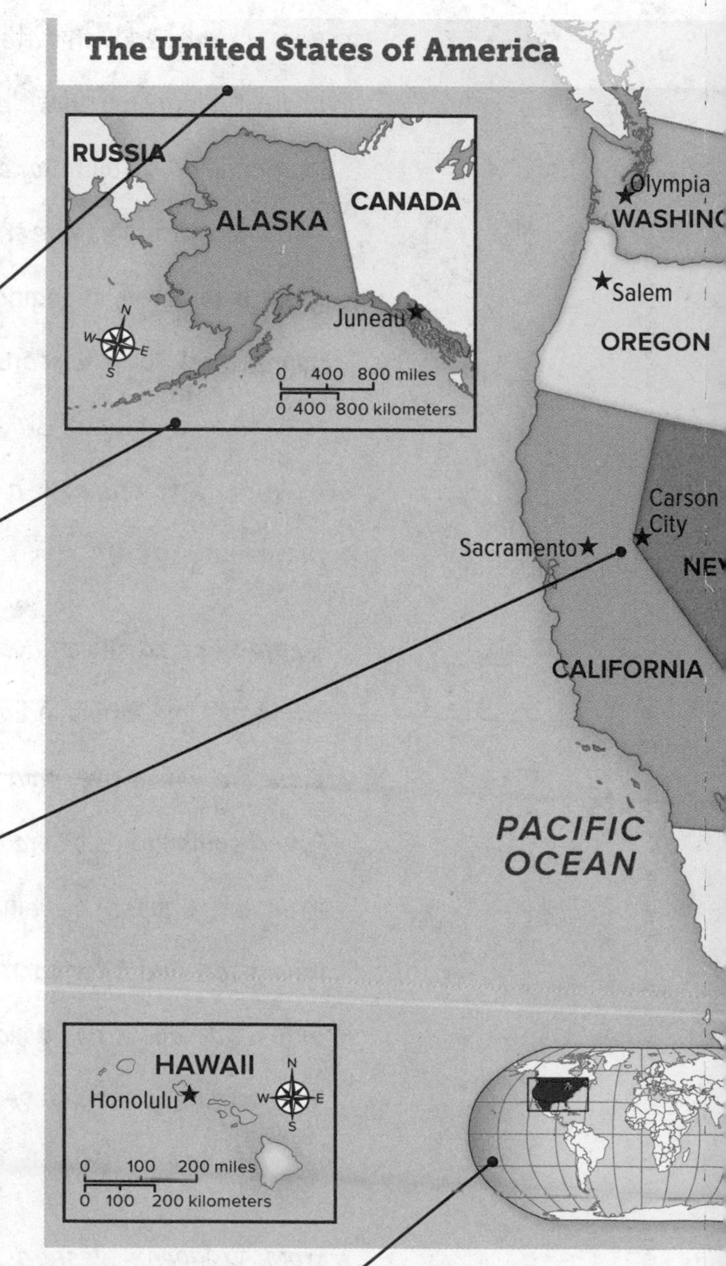

McGraw-Hill Education

Scale The scale shows the relationship between distances on a map and real distances. The line on this map scale covers 300 miles. One inch on the map is equal to 300 miles.

Compass Rose The compass rose shows where north, south, east, and west are on a map.

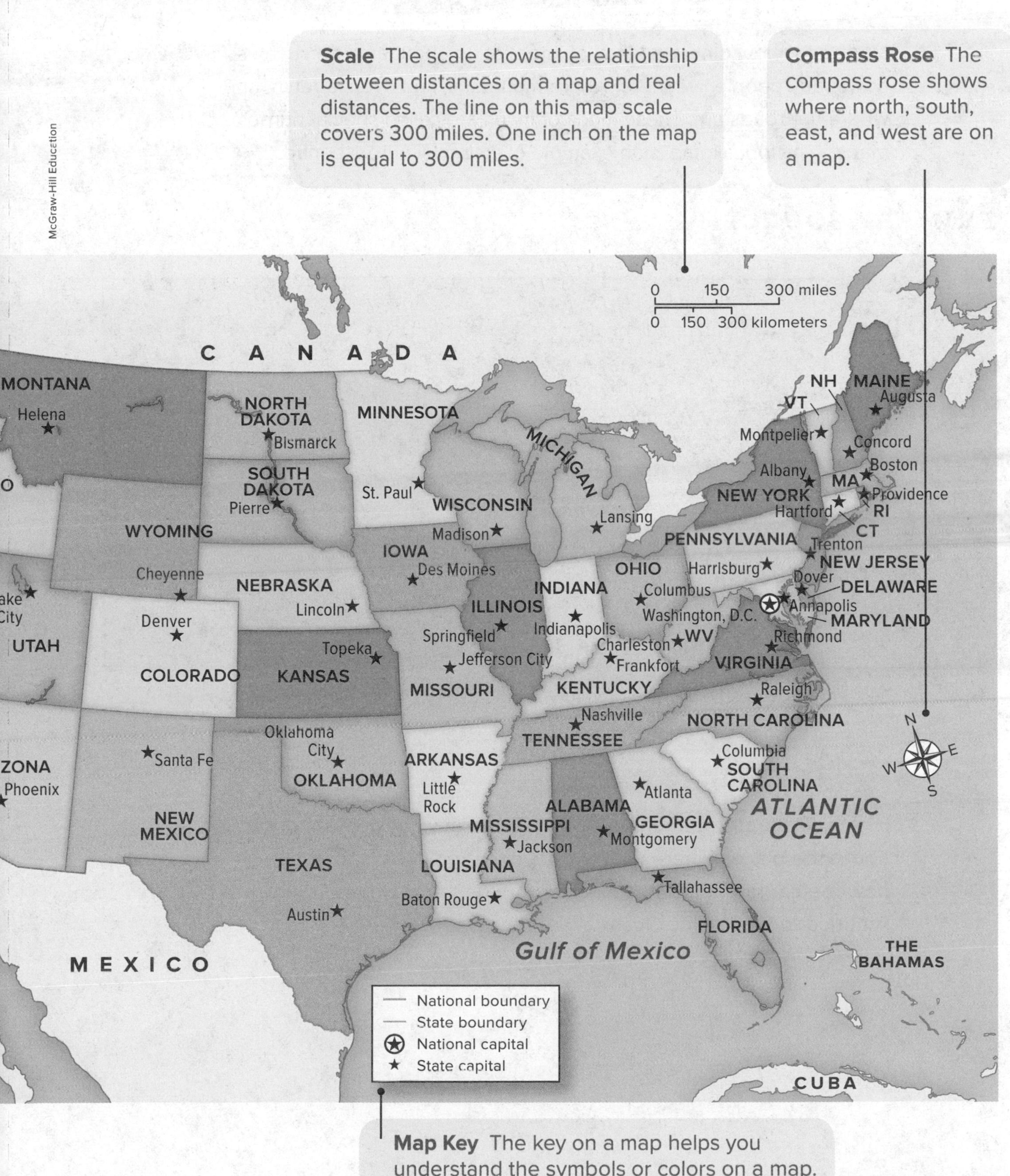

Map Key The key on a map helps you understand the symbols or colors on a map.

Special Purpose Maps

Maps can show different kinds of information about an area such as how many people live there, where mountains and rivers stretch, and where the roads are. These kinds of maps are called special purpose maps. A historical map is an example of a special purpose map.

PRIMARY SOURCE

Lewis and Clark's route across the Louisiana Territory

Historical Maps

Historical maps capture a period in time. They show information about the places where past events occurred. The map above shows how the explorers Lewis and Clark found their way across North America to the Pacific Ocean.

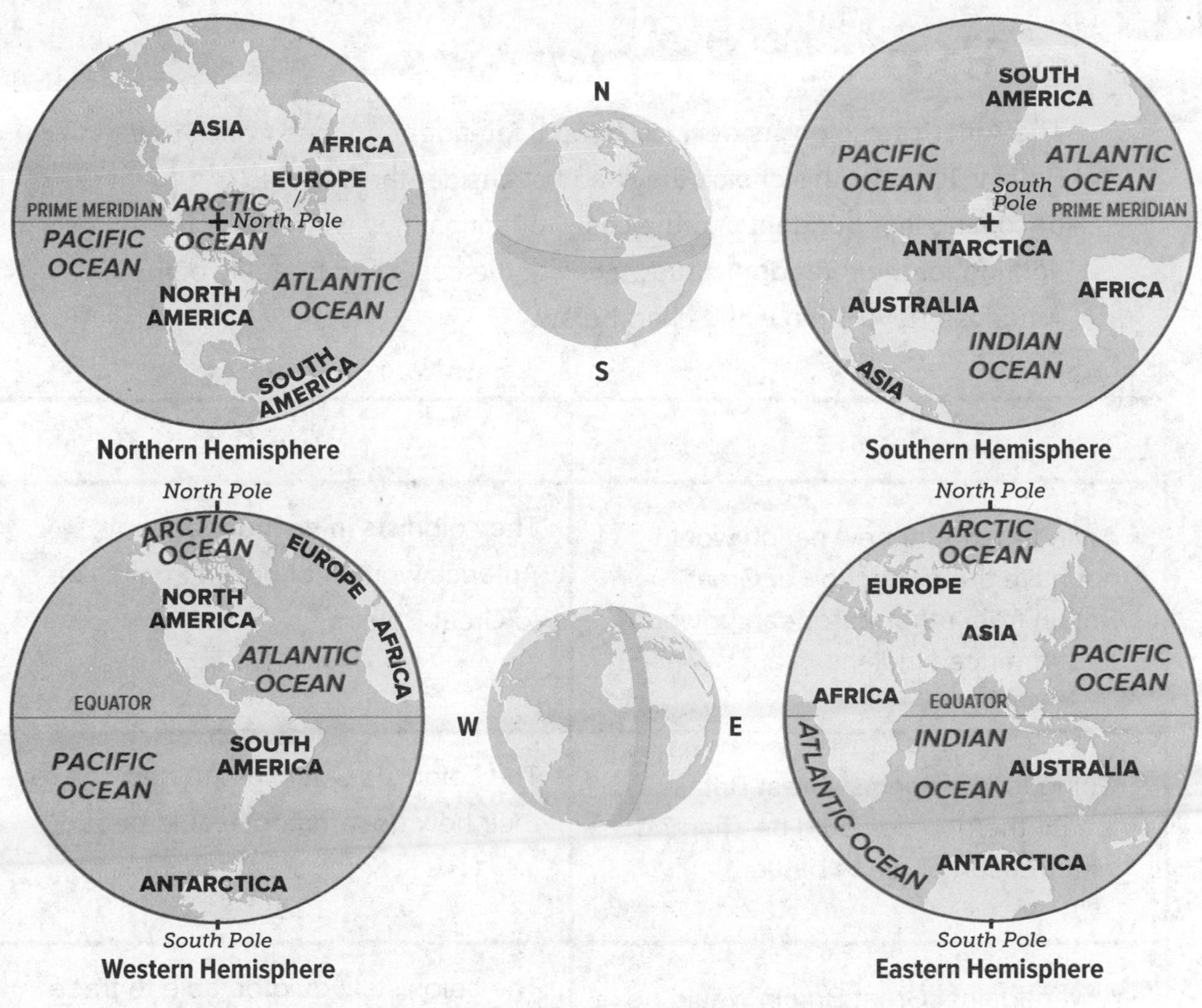

Looking At Earth

Another way to look at the earth is by using a globe. Geographers have divided Earth into northern and southern hemispheres at the equator. The area north of the equator is called the Northern Hemisphere. The area south of the equator is called the Southern Hemisphere. The prime meridian runs from north to south around Earth. The hemisphere east of the prime meridian is the Eastern Hemisphere. The hemisphere west of the prime meridian is the Western Hemisphere.

Explore Economics

The American colonists decided to fight for independence from Great Britain. To make this choice they had to consider the benefits of becoming independent and the costs, or things they would lose, in fighting for their freedom. Study a few of the costs and benefits of the American Revolution in the chart below.

Costs	Benefits
An independent new nation would not have the protection of Great Britain from other European powers and American Indians.	The colonists in an independent America would not have to pay taxes to Great Britain.
Going to war against Great Britain meant the people could be charged with treason or die in battle.	The colonists would get to decide how their new government would be run.
A war against Great Britain would be expensive and the colonists didn't have a lot of money to support the war effort.	The colonists would be able to trade goods and make deals with other countries.

Talk About It

If you were a colonist at the time of the American Revolution, would you have wanted to stay a part of Great Britain or fight to become an independent new nation? Use evidence to support your answer.

PRIMARY SOURCE

Currency from the period of the American Revolution

Explore Citizenship

You can learn to make an impact by being a good citizen. Some important words that define what it means to be a good citizen are listed on page 19a. They help us understand how to be better citizens in our home, neighborhood, school, community, country, and world.

Take Action!

You have learned to be a Social Studies detective by digging for clues and you practiced exploring and investigating geography, economics, and civics. Now it's time to explore the lessons in this book and make an impact!

PRIMARY SOURCE

President Lincoln at Antietam, Maryland, in 1862

Be a Good Citizen

COURAGE
Being brave in the face of difficulty

FREEDOM
Making choices and holding beliefs of one's own

HONESTY
Telling the truth

JUSTICE
Working toward fair treatment for everyone

LEADERSHIP
Showing good behavior worth following through example

LOYALTY
Showing support for people and one's country

RESPECT
Treating others as you would like to be treated

RESPONSIBILITY
Being worthy of trust

The Land and People Before Columbus

Where and How Did American Indians Live Before the Arrival of Europeans?

In this chapter, you'll read about how groups of early humans migrated across the Americas and formed civilizations. You'll learn about their cultures, and you'll understand how location influenced their ways of life.

COLLABORATE

Talk About It

Discuss with a partner what questions you have about the people who lived in the Americas before the arrival of Europeans. As you research early American Indian groups, look for answers to your questions. Let's get started!

My Research Questions

1. ______________________________

____

2. ______________________________

____

3. ______________________________

____

HSS.5.1.1, HSS.5.1.2, HSS.5.1.3, HAS.CS.5

Inquiry Project

Show what life was like . . .

A museum has asked you to design a display case for an American Indian group of your choice. Create a poster or diorama to showcase this group's daily life, including how the group obtained water, food, tools, clothing, and shelter. Show depictions of the group's religious and/or cultural traditions, government, and economy. Prepare a museum plaque to describe the visual. Then prepare a two-minute presentation.

Here's your project checklist.

- ☐ **Analyze** the task. Make sure you understand what you are expected to do.
- ☐ **Choose** an American Indian group from the chapter.
- ☐ **Conduct** research into the group's culture. Take notes.
- ☐ **Create** a poster or a diorama to show important information to visitors.
- ☐ **Write** a plaque for your poster or diorama.
- ☐ **Include** important points about the culture in a two-minute presentation.
- ☐ **Speak** slowly and clearly, and answer questions from your audience.

Explore Words

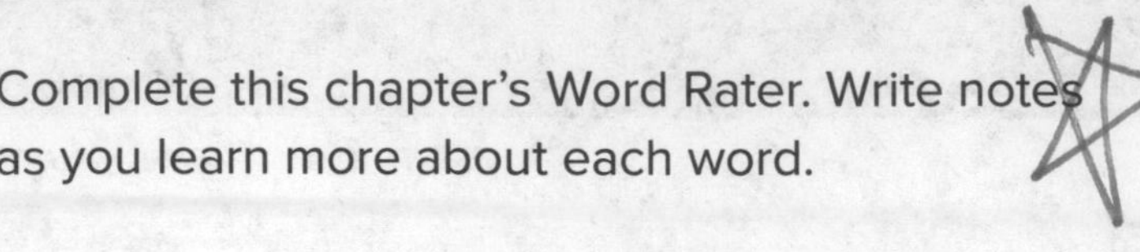

Complete this chapter's Word Rater. Write notes as you learn more about each word.

endeavor

- ☐ Know It!
- ☐ Heard It!
- ☒ Don't Know It!

My Notes
try hard to achive something

harvest

- ☐ Know It!
- ☒ Heard It!
- ☐ Don't Know It!

My Notes
the process of grabing crop

hieroglyph

- ☐ Know It!
- ☐ Heard It!
- ☒ Don't Know It!

My Notes
writing consisting of hieroglxphic

hunter-gatherer

- ☐ Know It!
- ☐ Heard It!
- ☒ Don't Know It!

My Notes
People who live by hunting.

mesa

- ☐ Know It!
- ☐ Heard It!
- ☒ Don't Know It!

My Notes
a isolated flat topped Hill with steep sides.

oral history

- ☐ Know It!
- ☐ Heard It!
- ☒ Don't Know It!

My Notes
The collection and study of
infousing sound.

potlatch

- ☐ Know It!
- ☐ Heard It!
- ☒ Don't Know It!

My Notes
Hold a pot latch

prairie

- ☐ Know It!
- ☒ Heard It!
- ☐ Don't Know It!

My Notes
a big space of grass

slash-and-burn

- ☐ Know It!
- ☐ Heard It!
- ☒ Don't Know It!

My Notes
aggresive

totem pole

- ☐ Know It!
- ☒ Heard It!
- ☐ Don't Know It!

My Notes
a pole on which totems
are hung on

How Did the Characteristics of Early American Indian Groups Develop?

Lesson Outcomes

What Am I Learning?

In this lesson, you're going to use your investigative skills to examine how early American Indian groups living in different regions developed special characteristics.

Why Am I Learning It?

Reading and talking about these early American Indian groups will help you understand how the regions in which they lived affected the development of their special characteristics.

How Will I Know That I Learned It?

You will be able to analyze information to identify the characteristics of early American Indian groups, give an opinion about how their surroundings influenced the development of these characteristics, and support your opinion with evidence.

Talk About It

Look at the Details The ancient structure in this image was built by early people. What do you think this structure was used for?

HSS.5.1.1; HAS.CS.4, HAS.CS.5

José Ignacio Soto/Shutterstock.com

The Kukulkan pyramid in Mexico was built by the Maya people.

Early Humans in North America

1 Inspect

Look Read the caption below the map. What do you think the term "land bridge" means?

- **Circle** words on the map that identify land areas and bodies of water.
- **Trace** possible migration routes followed by early humans.
- **Discuss** with a partner how the last Ice Age caused early humans to migrate into North America.

My Notes

Many major ice ages have taken place in Earth's history. During these periods, sheets of ice thousands of feet thick covered vast areas of land. With so much seawater trapped in ice sheets, or *glaciers*, sea levels dropped. Dry land appeared in some places. During the last major Ice Age, from about 30,000 to 12,000 years ago, sea levels dropped very low. A land bridge formed between the northeast tip of Asia and the northwest tip of North America. Scientists refer to this area as the Bering Land Bridge, or *Beringia*. Herds of Ice Age animals moved from Asia to North America across Beringia, looking for food. Many scientists think that early humans from Asia followed the animals they hunted across this land bridge.

Sometimes a hunting trip could take many days. The hunters had to gather plants to eat until they were able to kill an animal. The plants they gathered included berries, grasses, and mushrooms. This is why we call these people hunter-gatherers.

The Bering Land Bridge, or Beringia, linked Asia and North America during the last Ice Age.

Scientists think that humans first reached North America sometime between 30,000 and 12,000 years ago. Once in North America, these early humans may have migrated southward on land. Another possibility is that they avoided the ice by traveling in boats along the Pacific Coast.

2 Find Evidence

Look Again Underline words in the text that explain how the spread of glaciers during the last Ice Age caused Beringia to develop.

Examine Look back at the map. How does the map show the outline of Beringia? How does it show the outline of current landmasses?

3 Make Connections

Talk Using the symbols on the map, discuss with a partner the types of Ice Age animals that early human hunters followed into North America. What does this tell you about the hunting skills of these early humans?

Analyze Information

To analyze information means to break the information down into parts and then look at how those parts fit together. Analyzing information will help you determine what information means and how it will be useful.

1. **Read the text once all the way through.**
   This will give you a general idea of the subject, what kind of information is available, and how it might fit together.

2. **Look closely at the sources of information.**
   Do you trust that source will provide accurate information?

3. **Ask questions about what you are reading.**
   Questions such as *who, what, where, when,* and *why* can help you break the information down into parts.

4. **Note important patterns, relationships, and trends.**
   Taking note of important information in a graphic organizer can help you better interpret information.

Based on what you have just read about Beringia, work with your class to complete the chart below.

Location	Surroundings	Way of Life
Beringia and North America during the last Ice Age		

Investigate!

Read pages 8–17 in your Research Companion. Use your investigative skills to find information in the maps, images, and text that will help you understand the early American Indian groups living in one geographical area mentioned in the lesson. Use the chart to organize information.

Location	Surroundings	Way of Life
western hemisphere Beringal north america south west mexico, Belize and guatemala	the forest or wild ice age temples stone statchus placis unground houses adobe house mounds	hunter gathers the way of teamwork crop trading farmland handmade resourse

Think About It

Based on your research, how do you think the location and surroundings of the American Indian group you picked affected the way the people lived?

Write About It

Take a Stand

Write and Cite Evidence Write a brief, three-paragraph informational essay describing how the location and surroundings of the American Indian group you chose influenced the way the people lived.

Talk About It

Compare Your Groups

Talk to a classmate who chose a different American Indian group. What was similar about the ways your two groups lived? What was different?

Connect to the

Pull It Together

Think about the people you have learned about in this lesson. How would you describe the way American Indians lived before the arrival of the Europeans?

ESSENTIAL EQ QUESTION

Inquiry Project Notes

How Did the People of the Desert Southwest Meet Their Needs?

Lesson Outcomes

What Am I Learning?

In this lesson, you're going to use your investigative skills to learn about the cultures of the Pueblo, Navajo, and Apache peoples.

Why Am I Learning It?

Reading and talking about how people live in harsh desert conditions will help you understand how people adapt to their environment.

How Will I Know That I Learned It?

You will be able to compare and contrast different tribes of Southwestern American Indians and explain how their lifestyles allowed them to live in the desert.

Talk About It

Look at the Details Look closely at the picture. What meaning or purpose, if any, do you think these markings may have?

HSS.5.1.1, HSS.5.1.2, HSS.5.1.3, HAS.CS.4

milehightraveler/iStock/Getty Images

Petroglyphs at Penasco Blanco ruins

Navajo Ceremonies

1 Inspect

Read Study the translation of the Navajo song "Jó Ashílá." Then read the description of Navajo Ceremonies.

- **Discuss** with a partner why songs and ceremonies like "Jó Ashílá" and Enemyway are important to people.
- **Think** about special occasions when people might sing a song.

My Notes

"Jó Ashílá" is part of the Enemyway ceremony, a three-day-long ceremony meant to bring balance to the lives of the Navajo people. It can be performed for people who are ill or for individuals who have returned from war.

Singing and dancing are important parts of this and other ceremonies. There are more than sixty major ceremonies, including the Enemyway, the Blessingway, and the Navajo Night Chant. Some ceremonies can last more than a week and may contain more than five hundred songs. Dancers in masks help by representing various spirits in the ceremony. Sandpaintings, designs using brightly colored sands, are made specifically for each ceremony. The ceremonies are long and complex. So the singers who are qualified to lead them are highly respected.

Jó Ashílá

Hee yėe' yaa' a', hee yėe' yaa' a', Jó a-shí-lá,
jó a-shí-lá, jó a- shí-lá, hee yėe' yaa' a',
T'óó-gá ni-zhó-ní-go baa hó-zhó lá, hee ya hėe hee yá,
Jó a-shí-lá, jó a-shí-lá, jó a-shí-lá,
Hee yėe' yaa' ya', T'óó-gá ni-zhó-ní-go
łį̨į̨' gá N-dáá gi béézh ní'-áázh lá, hee ya hėe hee ya',
T'óó-gá ni-zhó-ní-go N-dáá gi łį̨į̨' gá béézh ní'-áázh lá,
hee ya hėe hee ya', Jó a-shí-lá, jó a-shí-lá,
jó a-shí-lá, hee yėe' ya wėi yaa' ya'.

English Translation:

Traveling together, Happy about beauty. It is beautiful that they both came on a horse at the Enemyway.

Special items used in an Enemyway ceremony

2 Find Evidence

Reread What is the song "Jó Ashilá" about? Circle words that help support this.

Examine Are the lyrics of the song meant to be taken exactly as it says? What else could this song mean? Why do you think this?

3 Make Connections

Talk Why do the Navajo perform these rituals?

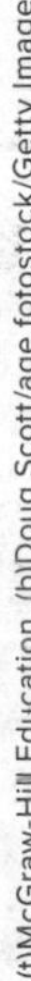

Explore Compare and Contrast

To **compare** is to find the similarities between two things. To **contrast** is to find their differences.

Similarities and differences can be linked. Two cultures may have similarities because they both came from the same group or they both live in similar environments. A difference in culture, however, could mean that one group has an advantage or hardship that the other group does not.

To compare and contrast:

1. **Read the text all the way through.**
   This will help you understand what the text is about.
2. **Look for keywords related to the information you want.**
   If you are looking for information about housing, look for words like *house*, *home*, and *build*, or materials like *wood* and *stone*.
3. **Summarize the information.**
   Make quick, simple answers to your questions.
4. **Review your answers.**
   Ask yourself, "*Which are the same?*" "*Which are different?*" "*Why?*"

Based on the text you just read, work with your class to complete the chart below comparing rituals and ceremonies.

	People in Your Community	**Navajo**
Rituals and Ceremonies		

Investigate!

Read pages 18–25 in your Research Companion. Use your investigative skills to look for text evidence that tells you about the lifestyles of different American Indian groups of the Southwest. Then, think about what is similar and what is different and why.

	Pueblo	Navajo	Apache
Housing			
Culture/Religion			
Economy			

Think About It

Review your research. Based on the information you have gathered, how did native peoples live in the deserts of the American Southwest?

Write About It

Write from Another's Perspective

Write a diary entry from the viewpoint of a Pueblo, Navajo, or Apache person. Be sure to include details about where you live, what you eat, what chores or jobs you do, and what possessions you have.

Talk About It

Discuss

In small groups, consider what you have learned about the American Indians of the Southwest. How have they adapted to life in the desert?

History

Connect to the

Pull It Together

Think about what you have learned about the lifestyles of the Southwest American Indians. What traditions continue to be used today? Why have these traditions continued?

Inquiry Project Notes

How Are the California and Pacific Northwest Peoples Shaped by Their Surroundings?

Lesson Outcomes

What Am I Learning?

In this lesson, you're going to use your investigative skills to find out how different groups of American Indians were affected by their surrounding environments.

Why Am I Learning It?

Reading and talking about the geographic features of California and the Pacific Northwest will help you understand the differences in the cultures of the American Indians who lived there.

How Will I Know That I Learned It?

You will be able to identify the relationship between where a group of people lived and the customs and practices of its culture.

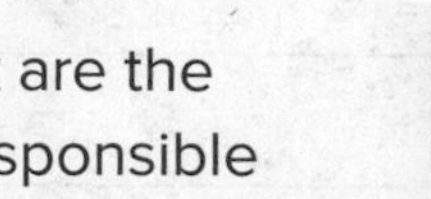

Talk About It

Look at the Details What task are the people at the back of the boat responsible for? What do the rest of the people do? Look for evidence that this is a ceremonial hunt.

HSS.5.1.1, HSS.5.1.2, HSS.5.1.3, HAS.CS.5

American Indians used to hunt from canoes along the Pacific Coast.

Chris Cheadle/Alamy

Analyze the Source

1 Inspect

Look Examine the image of a totem pole.

- **Circle** the figures depicted on the pole.
- **Discuss** with a partner what order the totems appear in and what they might represent.

My Notes

"Ridicule" totems, often used to shame individuals, appear upside down.

Bob Corson/Alamy

Totem Poles

The images carved on totem poles are often human, animal, or spiritual forms that represent something important to a family. For example, some American Indians have used wolves, eagles, and grizzly bears as symbols for their families. Totem poles have also been carved in honor of an important person or event. Today, these structures are associated with American Indians across the Pacific Northwest, but they originate with groups in southeastern Alaska such as the Tlingit and the Tsimshian.

Totem poles vary in height, but most are 10–50 feet tall. They can be placed in front of a family's home or beside a gravesite. Shorter ones may be kept inside the home. Totem pole carving nearly died out in the late 1800s when the U.S. government banned a number of American Indian ceremonies. American Indians revived the practice in the 1950s and continue to make totem poles today.

Totem-pole carvers usually make the poles from the wood of red cedar trees. Before a tree is cut down, native peoples may hold a ceremony of respect and thanks for the use of the tree.

On a pole the top totem, called a crest, often shows which clan the family belongs to. An upside-down totem is sometimes included to make fun of an enemy. Most totems have oval shapes. The carver may use colors or patterns in the wood to help determine designs.

2 Find Evidence

Infer What type of story might this totem pole tell? How do the totems and their order help tell that story?

Think Where would you place this totem pole in a village so that its message would be best delivered?

3 Make Connections

Talk Look again at the totem pole on the previous page. Pretend that your school is planning to build a totem pole outside the front doors. Like the Pacific Northwest peoples, your school wants the animals and people on the totem pole to welcome visitors and tell a story about the school's history. Which symbols would you include as totems? Which totems should be the highest on your pole? What story would you want visitors to know about your school?

COLLABORATE

Explore Compare and Contrast

You can better understand the ideas in a text if you **compare and contrast** the details the author provides.

1. **Read the text.**
   This will help you understand what the text is about.

2. **Think about how the text is organized.**
   If the text is divided into sections that each focus on a place or a group of people, look for topics that the author mentions in every section—for example, housing and customs. The author may be expecting you draw comparisons.

3. **Reread and look for text features.**
   Authors often use text features when they want to call attention to the similarities and differences between ideas. Analyze text features, looking at headings, bulleted texts, and images.

4. **Make notes in a chart.**
   You can use these notes later to help you remember what you read.

With the class, work to fill in one circle of the Venn diagram on page 27 using information about the Tlingit people from the previous page.

Investigate!

Read pages 26–33 in your Research Companion. Use your investigative skills to compare the Tlingit people with two other American Indian groups from this lesson. Consider where each group lived, its customs, and its artifacts. Write your findings in the diagram.

Tlingit People

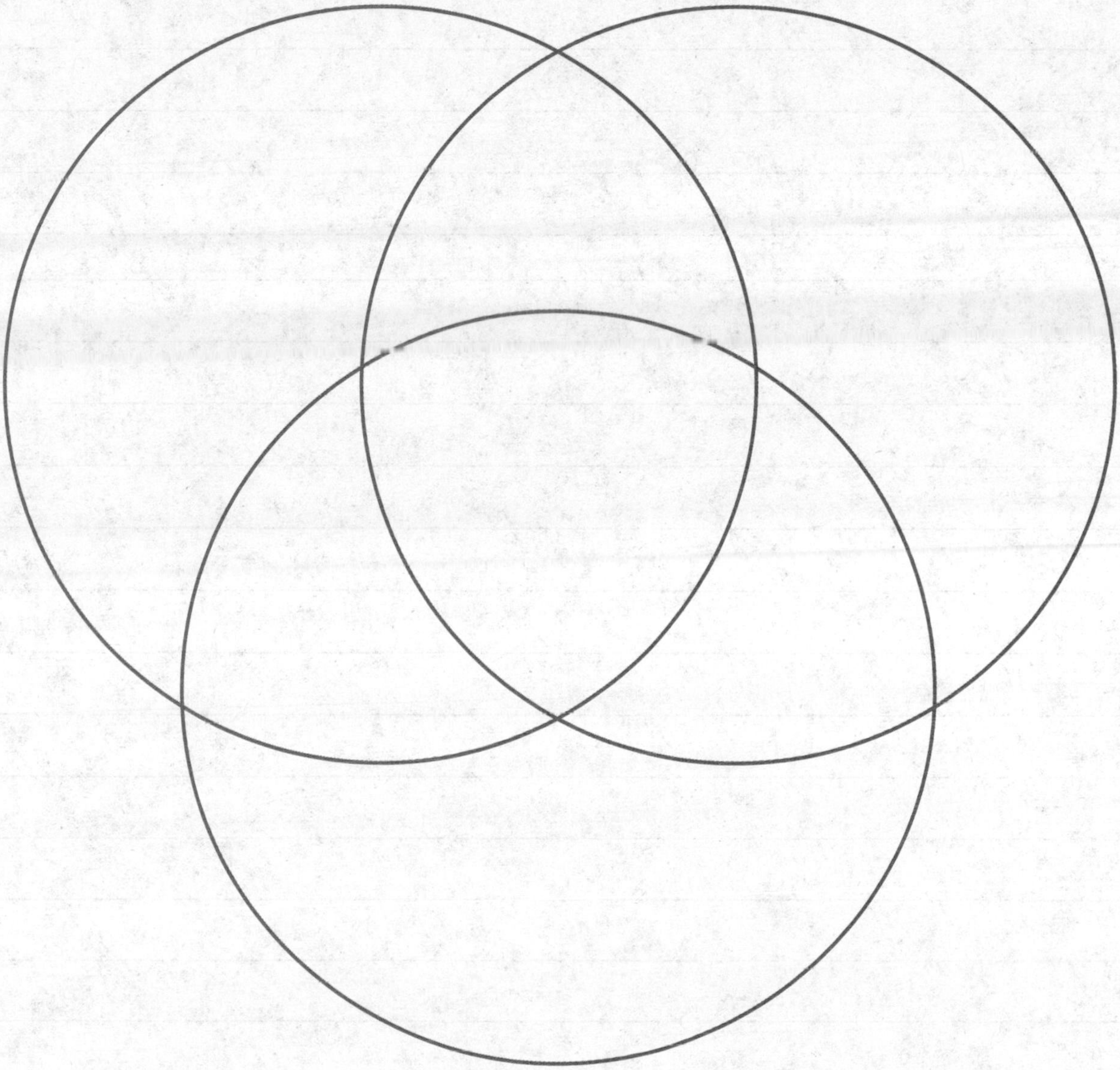

Think About It

Based on your research, what effect did plentiful resources have on the culture of American Indians in California and the Pacific Northwest?

Write About It

Take a Stand

Write and Cite Evidence Compare the artifacts and housing of two American Indian groups discussed in this lesson. In one paragraph, write an opinion about which group you think was best equipped to handle its surroundings and why.

Talk About It 

Defend Your Claim

In small groups, compare and contrast the American Indians you learned about this week with the groups from the Southwest deserts in Lesson 2. How does life in a desert and life in the Pacific Northwest affect culture?

Geography

Connect to the 

Pull It Together

Think about what you have learned about the American Indians of California and the Pacific Northwest. Consider the locations of major cities throughout the world. Explain why people tend to gather in certain areas using what you know about how American Indians of California and the Pacific Northwest were affected by their surroundings.

____

____

____

____

ESSENTIAL EQ QUESTION

Inquiry Project Notes

____

____

____

____

____

____

____

____

How Did the Great Plains Influence the Traditions of the People Living There?

Lesson Outcomes

What Am I Learning?

In this lesson, you're going to use your investigative skills to explore the traditions of the native peoples of the Great Plains.

Why Am I Learning It?

Reading and talking about where and how the people of the Great Plains lived will help you understand their traditions and ways of life.

How Will I Know That I Learned It?

You will be able to compare and contrast the roles of men and women in Great Plains groups to explain their traditions and ways of life.

COLLABORATE

Talk About It

Look at the Details What does the painting show? What role do you think the buffalo played in the lives of the Great Plains people?

HSS.5.1,1, HSS.5.1.2, HSS.5.1.3, HAS.HI.2

The people of the Plains depended on buffalo, more accurately called bison. Once horses came to the Americas, Plains hunters could move as fast as the buffalo could run.

Analyze the Source

Lakota Winter Count

1 Inspect

Look Examine the artifact on the next page. What can it tell you about the traditions of the Lakota people?

Discuss Talk about clues that answer these questions:

- Who made the artifact?
- What is the artifact made of?
- How was the artifact used?

My Notes

The winter count shown on the next page is an illustrated calendar created by the Lakota people of the Great Plains. Each year, Lakota leaders met to discuss the memorable events of the year. A pictograph, or symbol, that describes the most memorable event was then painted on an animal hide. Leaders would name the year based on that event. In this way, the Lakota could reference events by the name of a year. A keeper, who served as the band's historian, kept the winter count safe, year after year. Keepers were usually men. Women tended to have other responsibilities, such as making clothing and constructing teepees.

The artifact is called a "winter count" because the Lakota measured years from the first snowfall of one winter to the first snowfall of the next. This winter count recalls events that occurred between 1800 and 1871. The pictographs appear chronologically, starting at the center of the spiral. Some of the images depict events related to food and hunting, while others show battles with or visits from Europeans. For example,

- The first image on this page shows that Europeans brought striped blankets to the Lakota people in 1853–1854.
- The second image, at the bottom left, shows that the Lakota had plenty of buffalo meat in 1845–1846.
- The third image shows that 30 Lakota were killed by Crow Indians in 1800–1801.

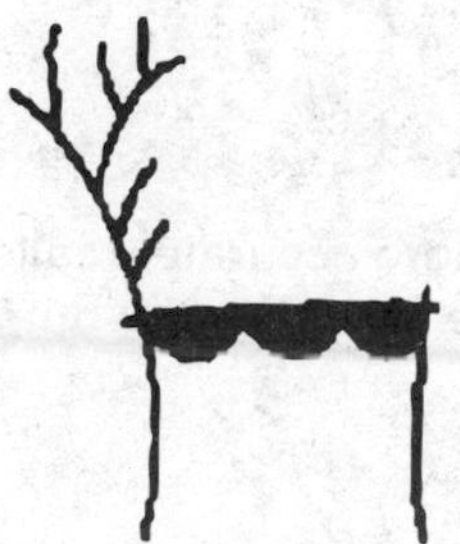

PRIMARY SOURCE

Winter Count by Lone Dog, 1801–1876

2 Find Evidence

Take Another Look How is the winter count organized? How does this organization help you understand the calendar?

3 Make Connections

Draw Work with a partner. Begin your own winter count that includes pictographs that show important events that have happened at your school over the past two or three weeks. Why did you include the events you did?

Explore Compare and Contrast

You can better understand the ideas in a text if you **compare and contrast** the details the author provides.

1. **Read the text.**
   This will help you understand what the text is about.

2. **Think about what the author wants you to know.**
   When you compare two things, you tell how they are the same. When you contrast things, you tell how they are different. Consider what the author wants you to know about similarities and differences between the roles of men, women, and children in Plains culture.

3. **Reread and look for text features.**
   Authors often use text features when they want to call attention to the similarities and differences between ideas. Analyze text features, looking at headings, bulleted texts, and images.

4. **Make notes in a chart.**
   You can use these notes later to help you remember what you read.

Based on the text you have read so far, work with your class to fill in some information in the chart below.

Roles for Plains Men	Roles for Plains Women

Investigate!

Read pages 34–39 in your Research Companion. Use your investigative skills to look for text evidence that tells you about traditional roles for Great Plains men and women. This chart will help you organize your notes.

Roles for Plains Men	Roles for Plains Women

Think About It

Review your research, and imagine that you are a blogger researching the Plains people. What were the most memorable things you learned about the Plains people?

Write About It

Compare and Contrast

Write an informative blogpost about the various activities and responsibilities of men and women in American Indian groups of the Plains.

Talk About It

Explain Your Thinking

Talk to a classmate about your findings. Take turns discussing how the activity helped you understand the differences between the roles of men and women among the Plains people.

Connect to the

Pull It Together

Think about the people you studied in this lesson. How were their lives shaped by geography?

ESSENTIAL EQ QUESTION

Inquiry Project Notes

McGraw-Hill Education

How Did the Eastern Woodlands Impact the Lives of Early People?

Lesson Outcomes

What Am I Learning?

In this lesson, you're going to use your investigative skills to explore how the American Indians of the Eastern Woodlands survived and lived.

Why Am I Learning It?

Reading and talking about the lives of American Indians living in this area will help you understand the problem-solving skills that allowed them to survive and thrive.

How Will I Know That I Learned It?

You will be able to describe the problem-solving skills of the American Indians living in the Eastern Woodlands, state an opinion about the most significant example of problem solving in the region, and support your opinion with evidence.

Talk About It

Look at the Details Examine the image and read the caption. Based on the image, what do you think the advantages of the longhouse were? Support your answer with details.

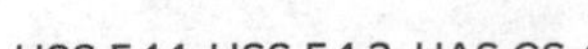
HSS.5.1.1, HSS.5.1.3, HAS.CS.4

The Iroquois lived in large homes called longhouses that held several families.

1 Inspect

Look Examine the illustration showing the outside and inside of an Iroquois longhouse.

- **Describe** the shape of the longhouse.
- **Identify** the material used to make the longhouse.
- **Discuss** with a partner why the Iroquois would have chosen to live in longhouses.

My Notes

The Iroquois Longhouse

While men sometimes built small wigwams while they were away hunting, the main type of housing for the Iroquois was the longhouse. These large houses took time to build. However, they were built from strong materials so that the Iroquois could live in permanent villages near the land they farmed. The walls were often made with saplings, which are strong and flexible trees that could curve to make the rafters. Large pieces of bark were used for the shingles.

The average Iroquois longhouse was 16 feet wide, 15 feet tall, and 60 feet long, but some houses could be as long as 300 feet. The longhouses had different compartments for different families. When a man married, he moved into his wife's longhouse to live with her extended family. These families were known as clans. As a clan grew, it could add compartments to its longhouse.

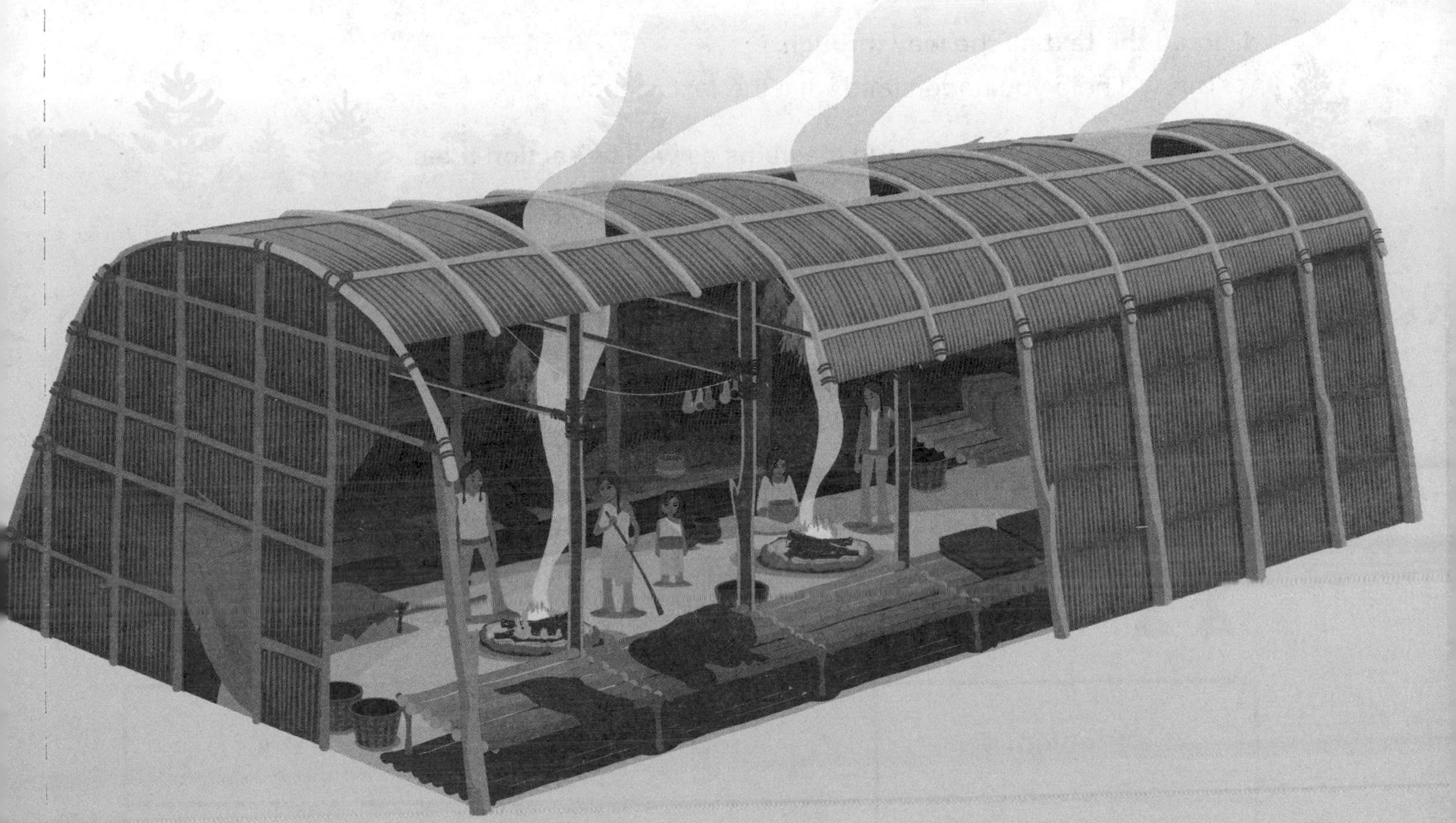

2 Find Evidence

Look Notice how the inside of the longhouse is organized. How would this organization make life easier for the people living there?

Examine Notice the bedding and the hallway of the longhouse. How do you think the structure of the longhouse affected the people living there?

3 Make Connections

Talk Discuss with a partner the different parts of the longhouse. What problems does each of these parts solve? Support your opinion with details from the illustration.

Write Describe what you like best about the design of the longhouse.

Inquiry Tools

Explore Problem and Solution

Identifying **problems and solutions** in what you read will help you understand the people you are studying and evaluate their ability to overcome challenges.

1. **Read the text all the way through.**
   This will help you understand what the text is about.

2. **Look at the illustrations and diagrams as well as section titles.**
   This will help you locate and understand important concepts.

3. **Think of the problems faced by the people you are reading about.**
   This will help you recognize solutions when you see them.

4. **Find key facts about the problems and the solutions.**
   While reading, ask yourself, *What details make this problem difficult to solve? What details about the solution make it work well?*

Based on the text you just read as well as illustrations and diagrams, work with your class to complete the chart below.

Problem	Solution	Key Details
How best to provide shelter		

Investigate!

Read pages 40–49 in your Research Companion. Use your investigative skills to identify problems American Indians in the Eastern Woodlands faced and the solutions they devised. Use the chart to organize your information.

Problem	Solution	Key Details

Report Your Findings

Think About It

Based on your research, how well did the American Indians of the Eastern Woodlands solve their problems?

Write About It

Take a Stand

Write and Cite Evidence In your opinion, what was the most significant example of problem solving in the Eastern Woodlands? List three reasons that support your opinion. Include page references.

Talk About It

Defend Your Claim

Talk with a classmate who chose a different example of problem solving. Take turns discussing your opinions and supporting evidence. Do you agree or disagree with your partner's opinion?

Geography

Connect to the

Pull It Together

Think about the people and events that you have read and talked about in this lesson. How did they solve problems posed by their environment?

____

____

____

____

____

ESSENTIAL EQ QUESTION

Inquiry Project Notes

____

____

____

____

____

____

____

____

Project Wrap-Up

Now's the time for you and your classmates to present your posters or dioramas. Here's what to do.

Use your notes to present on the American Indian culture you chose.

- ☐ Talk about the most important details and the most surprising and interesting facts you learned about the culture.
- ☐ Explain the group's culture and traditions, as well as its way of life.
- ☐ Point to your poster or diorama often, using it to illustrate the details in your presentation.

Tips for Presenting

Remember these tips when you present to your class.

- ☐ Be sure to prepare and to stay on topic when you speak.
- ☐ Speak slowly and clearly so everyone can hear you.
- ☐ Make eye contact and speak directly to your audience.

Project Rubric

Use these questions to help evaluate your project.

	Yes	No
Did I include the most important details about the American Indian group I chose?		
Did I consider the group's cultural and religious traditions?		
Did I create a poster or a diorama that is easy to understand?		
Did I create a two-minute presentation that summed up my research in a clear way?		
Did I speak slowly and clearly so my audience could understand me?		

Project Reflection

Think about the work you did in this chapter. What did you do well? What do you want to continue to learn more about? What would you do differently?

The Age of Exploration

Lesson 1
Dawn of the Age of Exploration

Lesson 2
Spanish Exploration and Conquest

Lesson 3
European Powers in the Americas

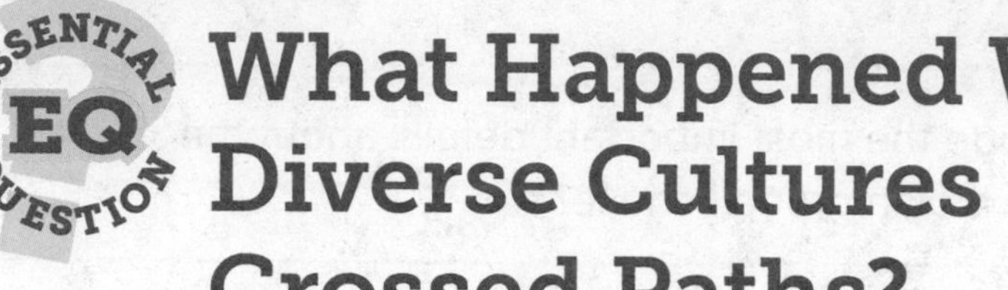

What Happened When Diverse Cultures Crossed Paths?

In this chapter, you'll read about why European powers decided to explore and claim parts of the Americas. You will also read about how European exploration affected the lives of the native peoples who lived there.

Talk About It

COLLABORATE

Discuss with a partner what questions you have about what happened to both the European and native cultures as a result of the Age of Exploration. As you research, look for answers to your questions. Let's get started!

My Research Questions

1. ______________________________

____

2. ______________________________

____

3. ______________________________

____

HSS.5.2.1, HSS.5.2.2, HAS.HI.3, HAS.HI.4

Inquiry Project

European Explorers: Collect Them All!

Choose a European explorer discussed in this chapter to research in depth, other than Christopher Columbus. Create a "trading card" for this explorer that includes an image depicting the explorer on the front. On the back, include important "statistics" or facts, such as where and when he was born, what led him to explore the Americas, and how his expedition impacted his country and the native peoples he interacted with. Then write a conclusion evaluating whether his actions were mostly positive or mostly negative.

Here's your project checklist.

- ☐ **Analyze** the task. Make sure you understand what you are expected to do.
- ☐ **Choose** an explorer from the chapter.
- ☐ **Conduct** research into the explorer's background and expedition. Take notes.
- ☐ **Create** a trading card with the explorer's picture on the front and information on the back.
- ☐ **Write** a conclusion that explains your conclusions about whether his actions were mostly positive or mostly negative.

Explore Words

Complete this chapter's Word Rater. Write notes as you learn more about each word.

charter

☐ Know It!
☐ Heard It!
☐ Don't Know It!

My Notes

claim

☐ Know It!
☐ Heard It!
☐ Don't Know It!

My Notes

colony

☐ Know It!
☐ Heard It!
☐ Don't Know It!

My Notes

conquest

☐ Know It!
☐ Heard It!
☐ Don't Know It!

My Notes

diverse

☐ Know It!
☐ Heard It!
☐ Don't Know It!

My Notes

merchants My Notes

- ☐ Know It!
- ☐ Heard It!
- ☐ Don't Know It!

navigation My Notes

- ☐ Know It!
- ☐ Heard It!
- ☐ Don't Know It!

resistance My Notes

- ☐ Know It!
- ☐ Heard It!
- ☐ Don't Know It!

settlement My Notes

- ☐ Know It!
- ☐ Heard It!
- ☐ Don't Know It!

warship My Notes

- ☐ Know It!
- ☐ Heard It!
- ☐ Don't Know It!

Why Did the Spanish Explore the Americas?

Lesson Outcomes

What Am I Learning?

In this lesson, you're going to use your investigative skills to learn how and why Spanish explorers first came to the Americas.

Why Am I Learning It?

Reading and talking about the lesson will help you understand the achievements of early Spanish explorers, such as Christopher Columbus, and how they affected the development of colonial America.

How Will I Know That I Learned It?

You will be able to use cause and effect to understand the developments that encouraged early Spanish explorers, such as Columbus, to sail to the Americas. You will be able to write an advertisement describing one of these technological developments and explaining how it would help an explorer on their voyage.

Talk About It

Examine the Details Read Columbus's letter that is translated into English. What does it show you about the goals or motives of the Spanish explorers who first came to the Americas?

5.2.2, HAS.HR.1, HAS.HR.2, HAS.HI.3.

Primary Source

In Their Words ... Christopher Columbus

. . . I gave [the inhabitants] many beautiful and pleasing things, which I had brought with me, for no return whatever, in order to win their affection, and that they might become Christians and inclined to love our King and Queen and Princes and all the people of Spain; and that they might be eager to search for and gather and give to us what they abound in and we greatly need.

—from a letter Columbus wrote to Queen Isabella and King Ferdinand as soon as he returned from his first voyage in 1493

TEXT: Christopher Columbus to King Ferdinand and Queen Isabella, March 14, 1493, Lisbon. Gilder Lehrman Collection #: GLC01427. Gilder Lehrman Institute of American History.; PHOTO: GL Archive/Alamy

Analyze the Source

1 Inspect

Look Examine this image. What does it depict?

- **Underline** words you don't know that are used as labels.
- **Circle** parts of the image that show you what those labels indicate.
- **Discuss** with a partner the kind of ship that Columbus sailed to the Americas.

My Notes

Diagram of a Caravel

The caravel was a small, light sailing ship. It was designed by the Portuguese and used by the Spanish in the late 1400s. Its lateen (triangular) and square sails caught the wind to help the ship travel faster. The caravel had a stern, or rear, rudder that helped it steer easily. It had a shallow keel, or bottom, that allowed it to go closer to shore than most other ships. It also had a large cargo hold to store supplies that were needed for a long journey. The *Niña* and the *Pinta*, two of the ships Columbus used to sail to the New World, were caravels.

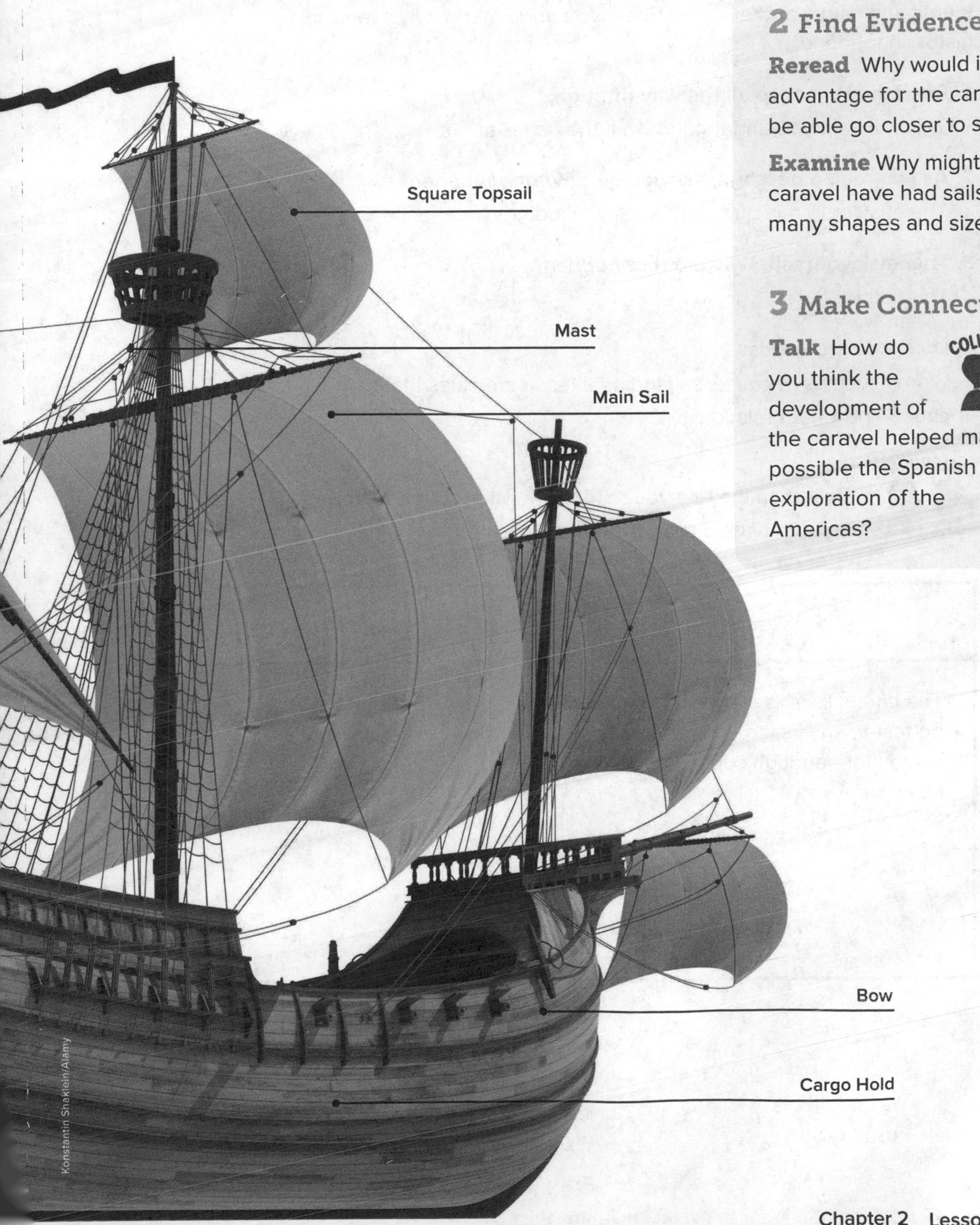

2 Find Evidence

Reread Why would it be an advantage for the caravel to be able go closer to shore?

Examine Why might the caravel have had sails of so many shapes and sizes?

3 Make Connections

Talk How do you think the development of the caravel helped make possible the Spanish exploration of the Americas?

COLLABORATE

Inquiry Tools

Explore Cause and Effect

Identifying **cause and effect** will help you understand why events in history happened.

1. **Read the text once all the way through.**
   This will help you understand what the text is about.
2. **As you read a passage, ask yourself, *What happened?***
   The answer to this question helps you identify an effect.
3. **Then ask yourself, *Why did that happen?***
   This is the cause.
4. **Look for clue words.**
   Words such as *because, so,* and *as a result* are clues that point to a cause-and-effect relationship.

Based on the text you read, work with your class to complete the chart below.

Cause	Effect
The caravel's sails allowed the ship to go faster, and its large cargo hold could store enough supplies for long journeys.	

Investigate!

Read pages 58–67 in your Research Companion. Use your investigative skills to identify the developments that helped cause Spanish exploration of the New World. Use the chart below to organize the information.

Cause		Effect
	→	
	→	
	→	
	→	
	→	

Report Your Findings

Think About It

Review your research about the developments that encouraged Spanish exploration of the New World. Which invention do you think was the most important? Why?

Write About It

Be Persuasive

Write an Advertisement Write an advertisement describing how the invention you chose works and why an explorer would find it useful. Find an image on the Internet to illustrate your ad.

Talk About It

Defend Your Choice

Review the goals of Spanish explorers. Then discuss how the invention you chose would help them achieve these goals.

Connect to the

Pull It Together

Explain how the invention you chose helped Spanish explorers like Christopher Columbus and how it might have affected the exploration and development of colonial America.

ESSENTIAL EQ QUESTION

Inquiry Project Notes

How Did Spanish Exploration Change the Lives of People in the Americas?

Lesson Outcomes

What Am I Learning?

In this lesson, you're going to use your investigative skills to learn how Spanish contact and exploration in the Americas changed the lives of the native peoples living there.

Why Am I Learning It?

Reading and talking about the effects of Spanish contact and exploration will help you understand changes that took place and that helped shape the Americas in the future.

How Will I Know That I Learned It?

You will be able to identify the causes and explain the effects of the Columbian Exchange and of Spanish conquest, exploration, and colonization of the Americas.

COLLABORATE

Talk About It

Look at the Details Examine the image of Cortés and his men. Based on this painting, do you predict their interactions with native peoples will end peacefully or violently?

HSS.5.2.1, HSS.5.2.2, HSS.5.2.3, HSS.5.3.1, HAS.CS.1, HAS.CS.2, HAS.CS.3, HAS.CS.4, HAS.CS.5, HAS.HR.1, HAS.HR2, HAS.HI.1, HAS.HI.3, HAS.HI.4

Hernan Cortés at Vera Cruz in 1519, where he decided to found a village.

Analyze the Source

1 Inspect

Look Examine this map. What types of items does it show?

- **Underline** plants that traveled between the Americas and Europe.
- **Circle** animals that traveled between the Americas and Europe.
- **Discuss** with a partner the effects that these items might have had on the peoples involved in the exchange.

My Notes

The Columbian Exchange

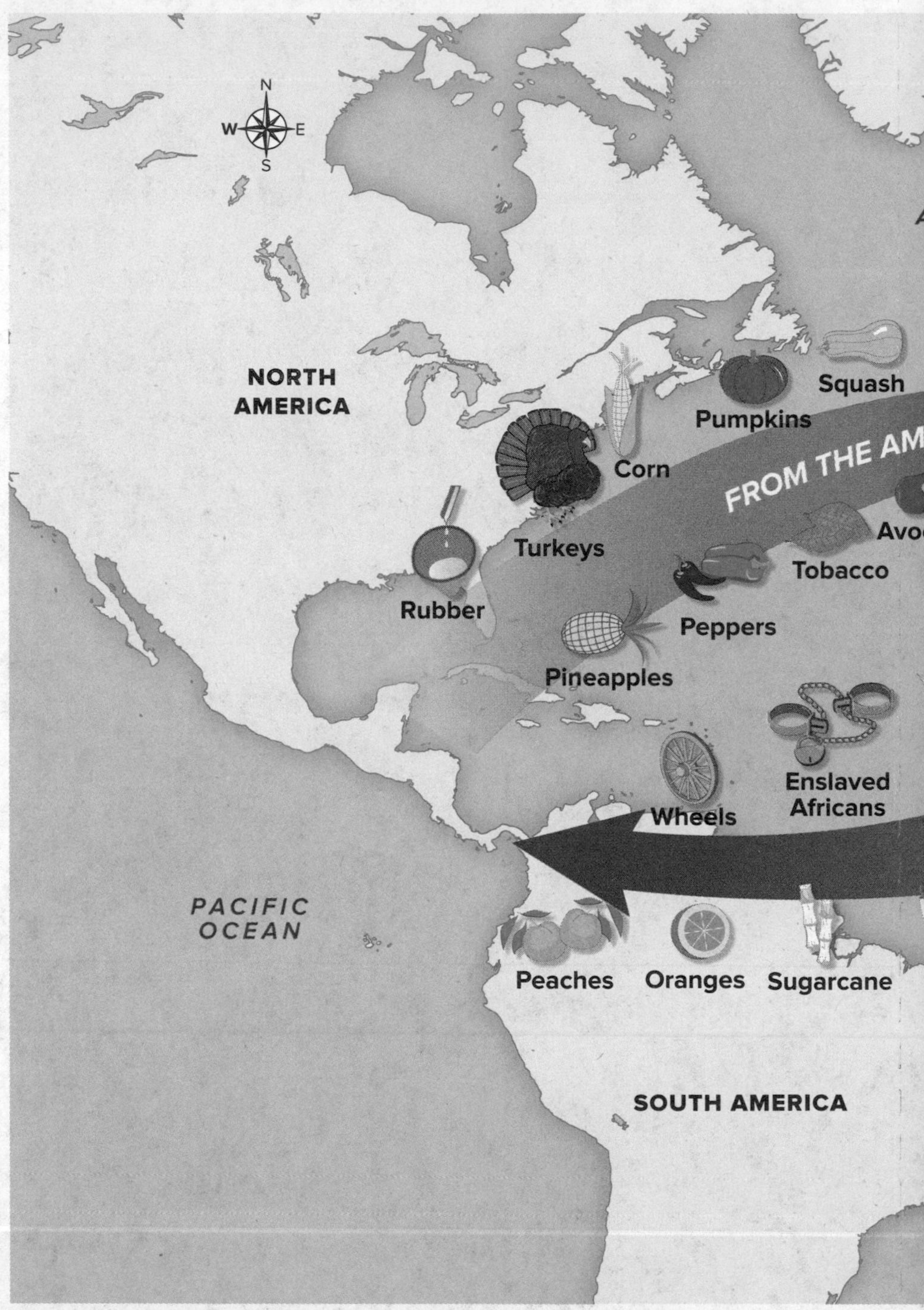

The Columbian Exchange changed life on both sides of the Atlantic Ocean. People in the Americas now had access to livestock, and Europeans were exposed to new food plants. The population in Europe grew, but many people in the Americas died as a result of diseases from Europe.

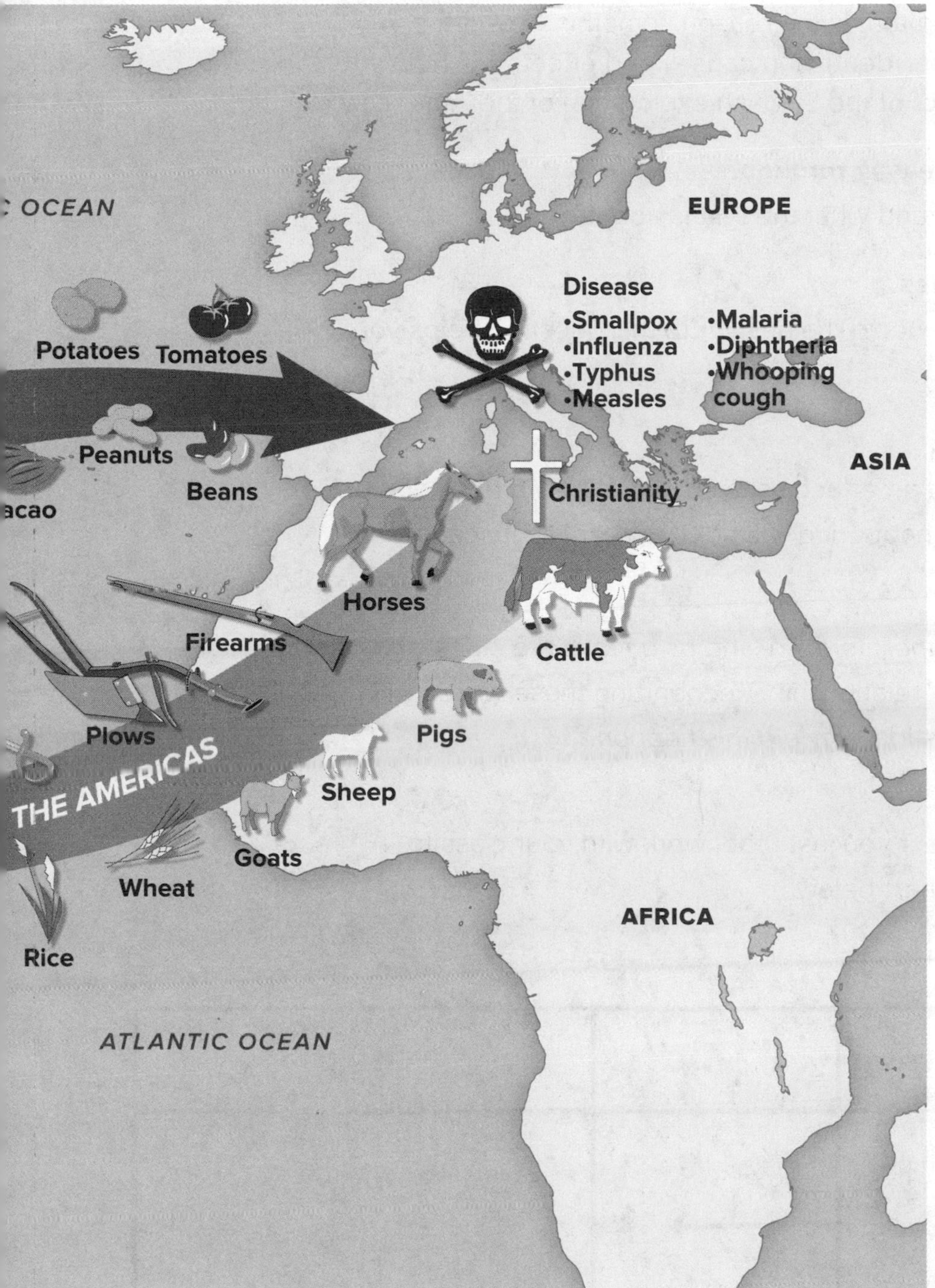

2 Find Evidence

Look Again Beyond items such as food and technology, what other things were exchanged? Were all of them beneficial?

3 Make Connections

Talk Which items do you think had the biggest effect on the lives of natives of the Americas? Why?

COLLABORATE

Explore Cause and Effect

A **cause** is an event or action that is the reason something happens. An **effect** is the result of a cause. Identifying causes and effects will help you better understand the impact of the Spanish exploration of the Americas.

1. **Read the text once all the way through.**
   This will help you understand what the text is about.
2. **Watch for specific changes.**
   Ask yourself, *What happened?* The answer to this question helps you identify an effect.
3. **Look for explanations.**
   When you have identified an effect, ask yourself, *Why did this happen?* Knowing why something happened will help you explain its cause.
4. **Look for clue words.**
   Words such as *because, therefore, so,* and *as a result* are clues that signal a cause-and-effect relationship. Recognizing these words will help you answer the question *Why did this happen?*

Based on the text you just read, work with your class to complete the chart below.

Causes		Effects
Many new food plants were introduced to Europe.	→	
Many diseases were brought to the Americas.	→	

Investigate!

Read pages 68–79 in your Research Companion. Use your investigative skills to determine causes and effects of Spanish conquest and colonization. Use the diagram below to organize the information.

Causes		Effects
	→	
	→	
	→	
	→	
	→	
	→	

Think About It

Your teacher will assign one of these explorers or conquistadors that you read about: Juan Ponce de Léon, Hernan Cortés, Francisco Pizarro, Alvar Nuñez Cabeza de Vaca, Hernando de Soto, or Francisco Vásquez de Coronado. Based on what you have read, how successful do you think the person was?

Write About It

Write an Essay

Choose a *different* explorer or conquistador than the one you were assigned. Write a three-paragraph informational essay about the impact the explorer or conquistador had on the native peoples of the Americas.

Talk About It

Share Your Ideas

Form a group with other students who wrote about the same Spanish explorer or conquistador. Discuss what was most significant about his achievements.

History

Connect to the

Consider a Different Outcome

Think about the details in the material you have read. From those details, how do you imagine native people's lives would have been different had the Spanish not arrived in the Americas? Would they have been better off?

ESSENTIAL EQ QUESTION

Inquiry Project Notes

How Did European Exploration Affect the Americas?

Lesson Outcomes

What Am I Learning?

In this lesson, you're going to use your investigative skills to explore how European exploration and settlement affected the Americas.

Why Am I Learning It?

Reading and talking about European exploration and settlement in the Americas will help you understand how the colonial period began and how native peoples were impacted.

How Will I Know That I Learned It?

You will be able to show an understanding of how Europeans affected the Americas by examining maps, and you will be able to demonstrate an understanding of how Europeans interacted with native peoples by writing about those encounters.

Talk About It

Look at the Details What seems to be happening? How do the people in the picture seem to feel about each other?

HSS.5.2.2, HSS.5.2.3, HSS.5.2.4, HSS.5.3.1, HSS.5.3.2, HAS.CS.4

Jacques Cartier meets American Indians in what is now Montreal, Canada.

A Shortcut to Asia

1 Inspect

Look Observe the map. What part of the world does it show?

Read Examine the map title, key, and text. What is the map about? What do the colored lines represent?

Circle Mark key information on the map and in the text.

- important words and dates
- names of explorers
- major labels on the map

Discuss What do you think the Northwest Passage was? Did explorers succeed in finding it?

My Notes

Many of the European explorers who reached North America between the late 1400s and early 1600s were really trying to get to Asia. Trade with Asia could be very profitable, especially when spices were involved. However, getting to Asia by sailing around Africa was difficult and dangerous. European rulers wanted to see if there was another way there.

The voyages shown on the map on the next page were paid for by the governments of England, France, and the Netherlands. The voyages took place between the years 1497 and 1611.

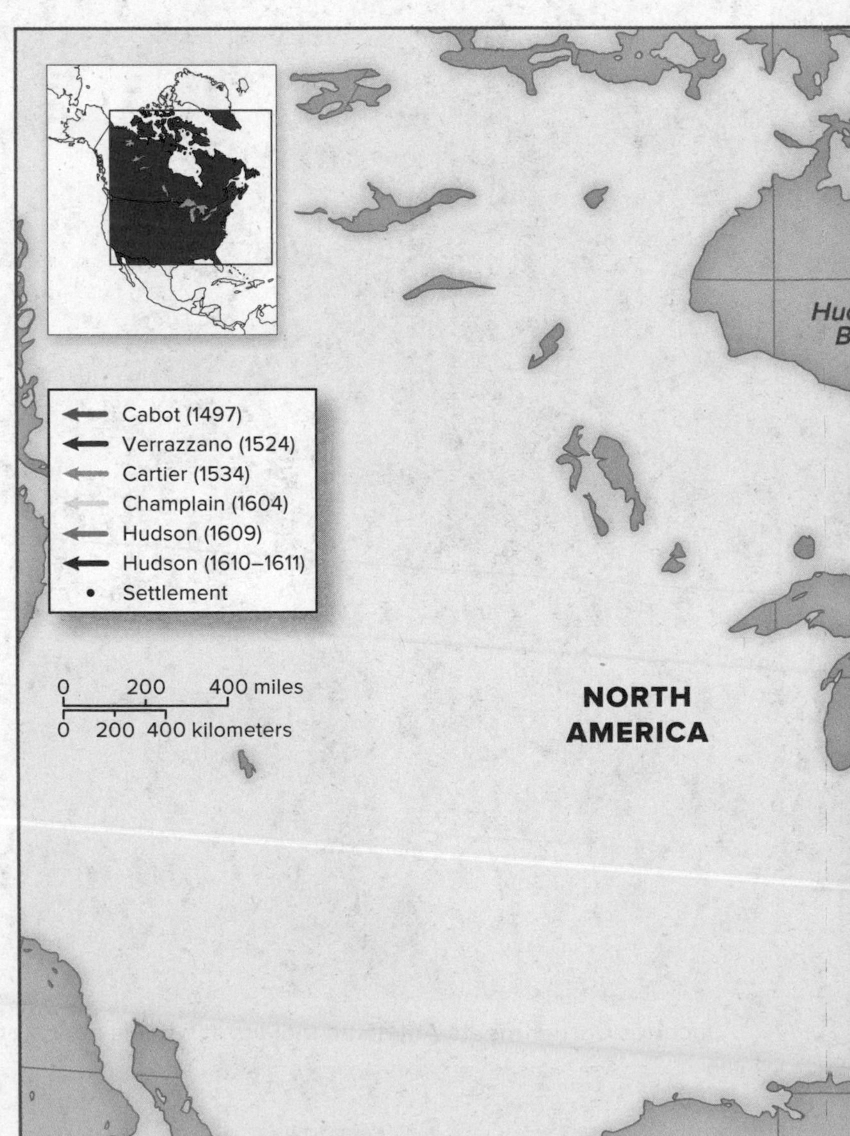

Europeans Search for a Northwest Passage, 1497-1611

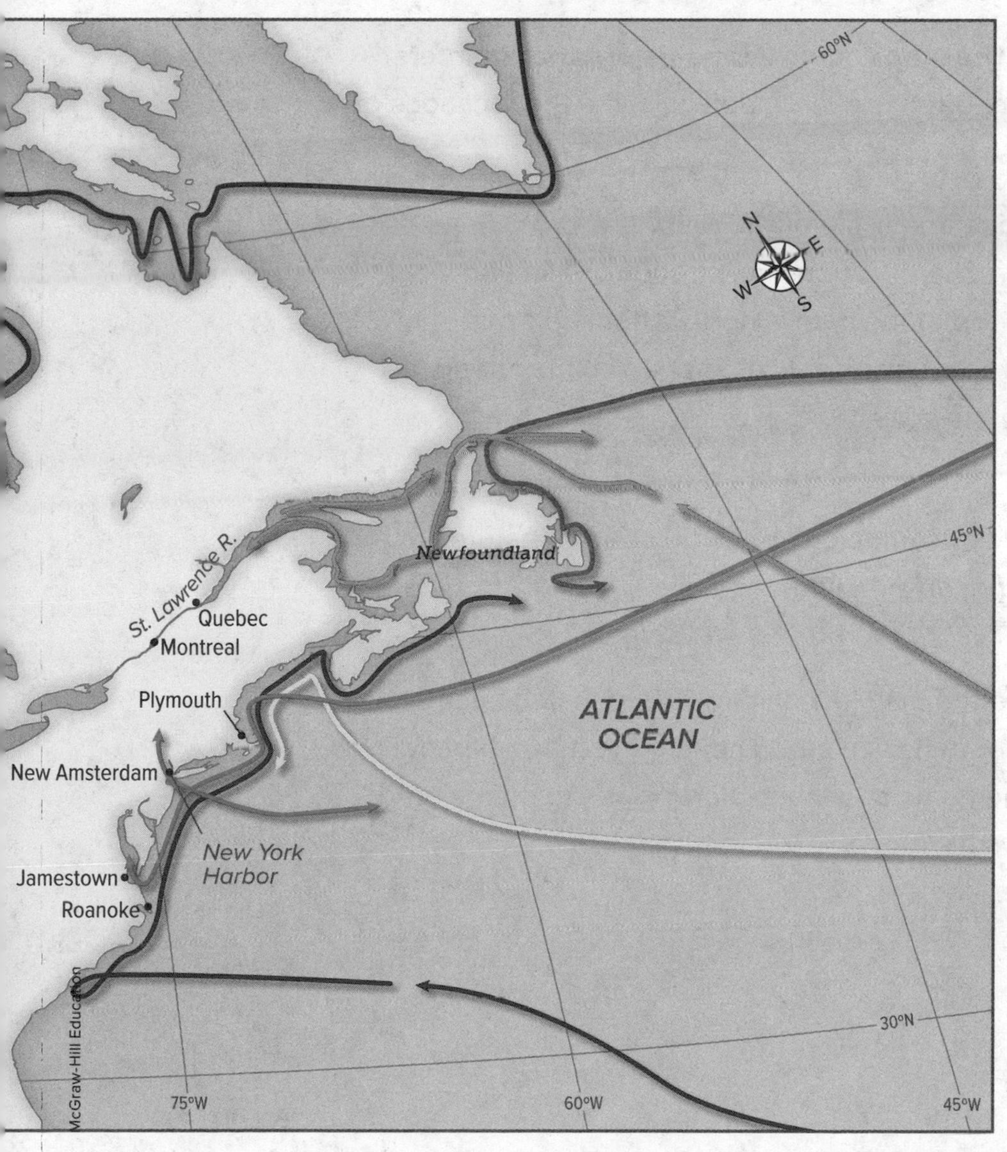

2 Find Evidence

Look Closely Using the information from the map, which explorer spent the longest time searching for the Northwest Passage?

Analyze Compare the route of Cartier in 1534 and the route of Hudson in 1610 with the other four routes. What makes those two routes different?

3 Make Connections

Discuss Talk with a partner. Give your opinion of which explorer came closest to finding a Northwest Passage. Give reasons to support your opinion.

Reading Maps

Maps can provide many types of information. Look at the map on the following page, and think about what information is being provided.

To analyze a map, follow these steps:

1. **Read the title of the map.**
   This should give you a good idea of the most important information the mapmaker is trying to provide.
2. **Read the labels on the map.**
   Note any differences in the size or style of the type. Larger labels may show major regions. Italic type may show bodies of water or other land features.
3. **Look for any places on the map shown with dots or other markers.**
   For example, mapmakers often use large dots to show the locations of major cities.
4. **Identify the compass rose and scale of the map.**
   The compass rose shows the directions north, south, east, and west. On almost all maps, the top of the map is north. The map scale shows the lengths used to represent miles or kilometers. You may need to use a ruler to determine the scale.
5. **Look for a map key.**
   This is a box that provides information about the special features of a map, such as color coding, dashed lines, or icons.

As a class, use the map key on page 70 to match each colored route with its explorer. Then on the map on pages 70-71, write the name of each explorer close to the colored line that shows his route.

Investigate!

Read pages 80–89 in your Research Companion. Use your investigative skills to look for text evidence that helps you fill in the missing information in the map key. Write the name of the country that claimed the territory shown by each color on the map.

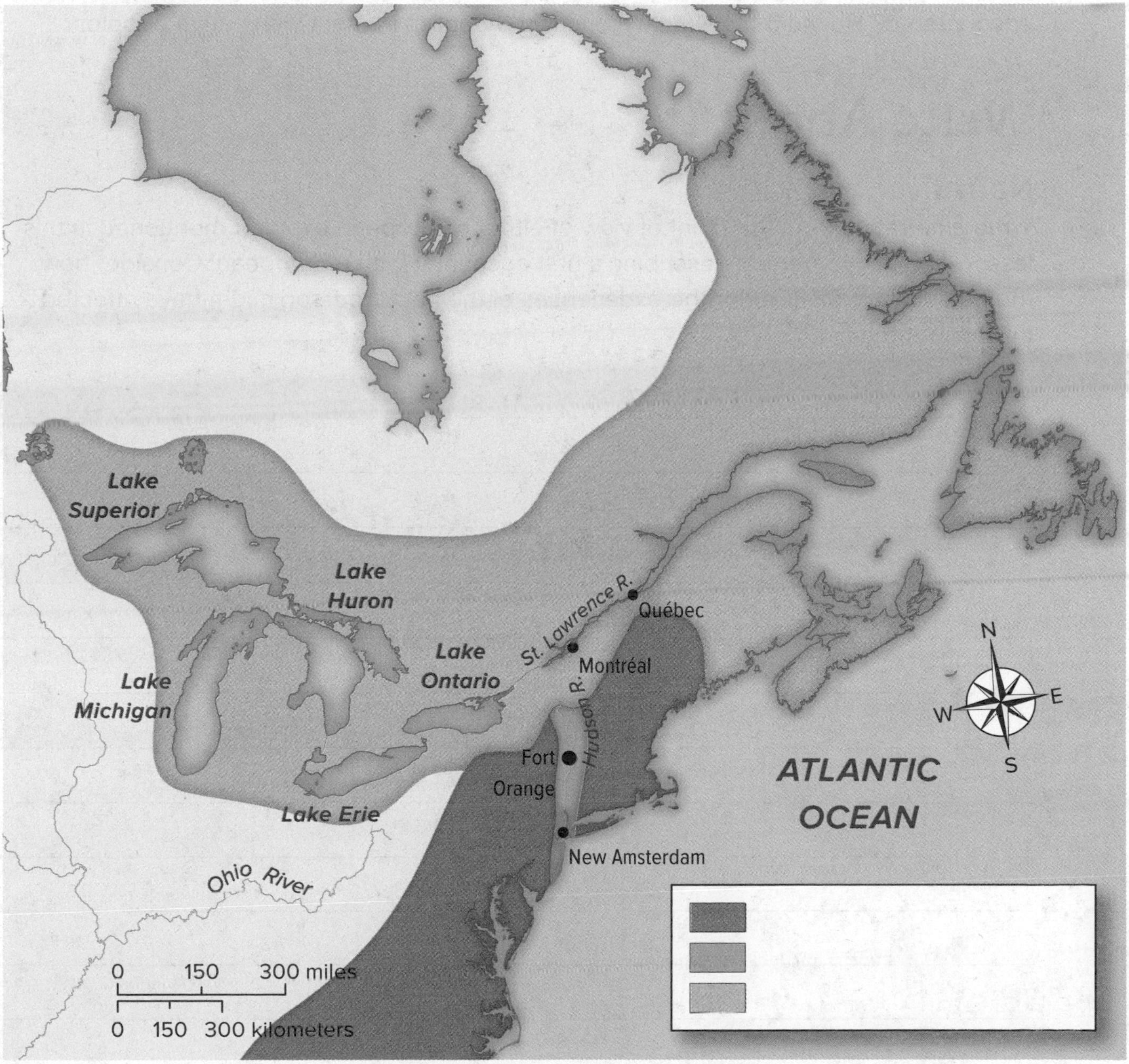

Lake Superior
Lake Huron
Lake Michigan
Lake Ontario
Lake Erie
Ohio River
St. Lawrence R.
Québec
Montréal
Hudson R.
Fort Orange
New Amsterdam
ATLANTIC OCEAN
N
E
S
W
0 150 300 miles
0 150 300 kilometers

Think About It

Review your research. Based on what you have read, what were the exploration goals in the Americas of the Netherlands, France, and England?

Talk About It

Compare the maps of European settlements in this lesson with the map on page 41 in your Research Companion. Which native groups might the Europeans have encountered? How did the Dutch, French, and English interact with native peoples?

Write About It

Narrative

Write a narrative from the point of view of either a European explorer mentioned in this lesson or a native person describing a first encounter with a European. Consider how the goals of the explorer or the experiences of the native person might have affected this encounter.

History

Connect to the 

Contrast

Looking back over the chapter, discuss how the relationships between American Indians and the various European explorers differed.

EQ ESSENTIAL QUESTION

Inquiry Project Notes

Project Wrap-Up

Now's the time for you and your classmates to present your trading cards. Here's what to do.

Use your notes to present on the European explorer you chose.

- ☐ Project or hand out copies of the front and back of your trading card.
- ☐ Talk about the most important and interesting facts about your explorer.
- ☐ Explain the effects of the explorer's expedition on his home country or sponsor country and on the native peoples he encountered.
- ☐ Refer to your trading card often, using it to illustrate the details in your presentation.

Tips for Presenting

Remember these tips when you present to your class.

- ☐ Provide details about your explorer in a logical order, such as time order or cause and effect.
- ☐ Give descriptive details that will be interesting to your audience.
- ☐ Speak slowly so your audience can understand you.

Project Rubric

Use these questions to help evaluate your project.

	Yes	No
Did I include both a picture and facts or statistics about my explorer?		
Did I include important and interesting details about my explorer?		
Did I draw conclusions about whether my explorer's influence was mostly positive or mostly negative?		
Did I present the most important and interesting details about my explorer?		
Did I speak slowly and clearly so my audience could understand me?		

Project Reflection

Think about your work during this chapter. What did you enjoy most? What do you want to continue to learn about? What will you do differently in your work on the next chapter?

____

____

____

____

____

____

____

A Changing Continent

How Did European Settlements Impact North America?

In this chapter, you'll learn how European settlements affected the land and native peoples of North America. You'll learn about how England, France, and Spain competed for land and power in the New World, and you'll identify how relations with American Indian groups influenced the success of each settlement.

COLLABORATE

Talk About It

Discuss with a partner what questions you have about how European settlements developed in North America and how those settlements affected the continent as well as American Indians. As you research, look for answers to your questions. Let's get started!

My Research Questions

1. ______________________________

____

2. ______________________________

____

3. ______________________________

____

HSS.5.3.1, HSS.5.3.2, HSS.5.3.3, HAS.HI.3

Inquiry Project

Tell Both Sides of the Story

Write a short narrative that illustrates the relations between a specific group of European settlers and the American Indians they encountered. Describe events clearly from both sides, using effective dialogue and descriptions. Identify the effects of those relations on the American Indians' way of life as well as the benefits or setbacks the Europeans experienced. Working with a small group, read each other's stories aloud.

Here's your project checklist.

- ☐ **Analyze** the task. Make sure you understand what you are expected to do.
- ☐ **Choose** a settlement discussed in the chapter.
- ☐ **Conduct** research into the settlement's origin and relations with local American Indians. Take notes.
- ☐ **Write** a narrative about these relations, using details and facts from the text.
- ☐ **Work** with a small group to read aloud each other's narratives.
- ☐ **Discuss** the effects of the settlement's relations with the American Indian groups on the success or failure of the settlement as a whole.

Explore Words

Complete this chapter's Word Rater. Write notes as you learn more about each word.

assembly
- ☐ Know It!
- ☐ Heard It!
- ☐ Don't Know It!

My Notes

cash crop
- ☐ Know It!
- ☐ Heard It!
- ☐ Don't Know It!

My Notes

commerce
- ☐ Know It!
- ☐ Heard It!
- ☐ Don't Know It!

My Notes

covenant
- ☐ Know It!
- ☐ Heard It!
- ☐ Don't Know It!

My Notes

demand
- ☐ Know It!
- ☐ Heard It!
- ☐ Don't Know It!

My Notes

dissension

My Notes

☐ Know It!
☐ Heard It!
☐ Don't Know It!

encomiendas

My Notes

☐ Know It!
☐ Heard It!
☐ Don't Know It!

environment

My Notes

☐ Know It!
☐ Heard It!
☐ Don't Know It!

missionary

My Notes

☐ Know It!
☐ Heard It!
☐ Don't Know It!

proprietor

My Notes

☐ Know It!
☐ Heard It!
☐ Don't Know It!

How Did Early English Settlers Cooperate and Clash with American Indians?

Lesson Outcomes

What Am I Learning?

In this lesson, you're going to use your investigative skills to understand the history of England's first permanent colony in North America and how the colonists affected and were affected by American Indians.

Why Am I Learning It?

Reading and talking about the Jamestown colony will help you learn how different cultures interact and how actions and decisions are connected.

How Will I Know That I Learned It?

You will be able to explain the causes and effects of Jamestown's failures and successes.

Talk About It

Look at the Map What features do you notice about the settlement? What is the importance of these features?

HSS.5.3.1, HSS.5.3.2, HSS.5.3.3, HSS.5.4.1, HAS.HR.2

James Fort at Jamestown settlement

The Starving Time

1 Inspect

Read First read the introductory text, and then read the quotation in the Primary Source box. How are they related?

- **Circle** words used in ways that are different from the ways they are most often used. Try to determine their meaning from context.
- **Discuss** with a group whether the starving time could have been prevented if John Smith had not been injured.

My Notes

George Percy

In 1609, Captain John Smith was wounded in a gunpowder accident. His injuries forced him to return to England, and a noble named George Percy took his place as the leader of the Jamestown colony. Smith had played a key role in improving relations with the Powhatan Indians and ensuring the colonists worked hard. Without him, they were unprepared for a drought later that year, and Chief Powhatan refused to help them. Although Chief Powhatan had liked and respected Smith, he did not feel the same about other settlers. In fact, he was insulted when the Virginia Company gifted him with a crown to mark him as a prince under the rule of King James. Furthermore, his own people were hurt by the drought. Seeing the colony as weak and vulnerable, the Powhatan leader decided to starve the settlers into abandoning their colony, ordering his men to kill any colonist attempting to hunt or gather food outside of the fort. By the spring of 1610, only 60 colonists remained at Jamestown.

PRIMARY SOURCE

In Their Words... George Percy

Jamestown "Starving Time"

Now all of us at James Town, beginning to feel that sharp prick of hunger which no man truly describe but he which has tasted the bitterness thereof, a world of miseries ensued as the sequel will express unto you, in so much that some to satisfy their hunger have robbed the store for the which I caused them to be executed.

Then having fed upon horses and other beasts as long as they lasted, we were glad to make shift with vermin as dogs, cats, rats, and mice. All was fish that came to net to satisfy cruel hunger as to eat boots, shoes, or any other leather some could come by, and, those being spent and devoured, some were enforced to search the woods and to feed upon serpents and snakes and to dig the earth for wild and unknown roots, where many of our men were cut off of and slain by the savages.

—from George Percy's *A True Relation—A Trewe Relacyon*, written in the mid-1620s.

2 Find Evidence

Reread What details does George Percy include in his account to support the idea that the colony was starving? Why are these details effective?

What is meant by the statement "All was fish that came to net to satisfy cruel hunger"? Is Percy referring to actual fish?

3 Make Connections

COLLABORATE

Talk What was the main cause of the Starving Time? Discuss and defend your opinion with your group.

What long-term effects do you think the Starving Time had on the colony?

Inquiry Tools

Explore Cause and Effect

Some of the events you will read about in this lesson have cause-and-effect relationships. To better understand history, it is important to know about cause and effect. The causes of historical events explain why things happened, and the effects of events show why the events are important to people afterwards.

1. **Look for transitions related to causes and effects.**
   Because, therefore, as a result, in order to, and similar transitional words and phrases can indicate cause-and-effect relationships.

2. **Take note of chronology.**
   Texts will often present cause-and-effect relationships in the order that the two events happen. This is not always true, though, so be careful.

3. **Analyze the events.**
   Would an event have happened without this particular cause? Would the effect have been the same if the earlier event had never happened? Ask yourself questions like these to determine how strong the relationship between two events is.

4. **Note that an event may have more than one cause or effect.**

Based on the text you just read, work with your class to complete the chart below.

Cause		Effect
John Smith returned to England.	→	

Investigate!

Read pages 100–109 in your Research Companion. Use your investigative skills to identify cause-and-effect relationships in the text. Find events in the text that led to improved or worsened relations between the colonists and the Powhatan. Each event will be the "cause," while what happened as a result of each event is the "effect." Use this information to fill in the graphic organizer below.

Cause		Effect
	→	
	→	
	→	
	→	

Think About It

Review your research. Based on the information you have gathered, did the settlers' relationship with American Indians ultimately help or hurt the Jamestown Colony?

Write About It

Take a Stand

Write and Cite Evidence Defend your idea by identifying at least three examples from Jamestown's history that indicate whether the relationship with American Indians helped or harmed the Jamestown settlement. Use evidence from the text to support your opinion.

Talk About It 

Defend Your Claim

Choose a partner who disagrees with you about the relationship between the Powhatan and the settlers. Work together to outline your difference of opinion. Did your partner's claim change your thinking about your own claim?

Connect to the 

Pull It Together

Think about the changing relationship between the English settlers and the Powhatan people. How might this relationship have shaped future interaction between English colonists and American Indians?

____

____

____

____

____

____

____

____

ESSENTIAL EQ QUESTION

Inquiry Project Notes

____

____

____

____

____

____

Lesson 2 How Did Early European Settlers Compete with One Another and American Indians?

Lesson Outcomes

What Am I Learning?

In this lesson, you're going to use your investigative skills to explore how European colonists competed with one another and American Indians.

Why Am I Learning It?

Reading and talking about competition among European settlers and American Indians will help you understand how and why the different groups attempted to gain power over one another.

How Will I Know That I Learned It?

You will be able to explain the different strategies of European and American Indian groups in the Americas and evaluate the economic results of their efforts.

COLLABORATE

Talk About It

Look at the Details Which groups are involved in the battle? Who is fighting whom?

HSS.5.3.1, HSS.5.3.2; HAS.CS.4, HAS.HI.3

Samuel de Champlain's men allied with Algonquin Indians fighting an Iroquois war party

The Saint Lawrence: At the Heart of New France

1 Inspect

Read Look at the title. What do you think this text will be about?

- **Circle** words you don't know.
- **Underline** clues that help answer these questions:
  - Where is the Saint Lawrence River?
  - Who used the river?
  - Why was it important?

My Notes

The Saint Lawrence River connects the Great Lakes to the Atlantic Ocean. French explorers hoped that the Saint Lawrence could take them all the way across North America. The river did not do so. However, it did supply a route for trade and exploration of Canada and what is now the northern United States.

Samuel de Champlain was one of the first Europeans to sail the river in 1603. At the time, he called it the River of Canada. Champlain published a report of his travels in France. Champlain's writings inspired more support for the exploration of the Saint Lawrence. In 1608, Champlain and a group of colonists settled along the river, naming the region Quebec.

The colony of New France used this lengthy waterway to transport furs and other trade goods. From trading posts as far inland as Chicago and Detroit, the colonists could easily move goods to and across the Atlantic Ocean. Since people tend to live close to water, the Saint Lawrence also allowed the French to establish relationships with many of the American Indian groups of the region. This Saint Lawrence trade network played a major role in the economy of New France.

Samuel de Champlain arrives at the site of Quebec City along the Saint Lawrence River.

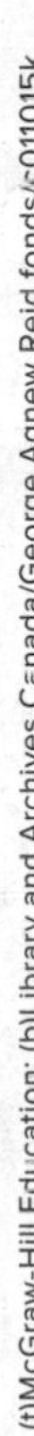

2 Find Evidence

Reread List three reasons why the Saint Lawrence River was important to New France.

Underline the names of places connected by the Saint Lawrence River.

3 Make Connections

Talk Do you think American Indians likely benefited or suffered as a result of the Saint Lawrence trade network?

How does the picture help you understand how French sailors navigated the Saint Lawrence?

Explore Main Ideas and Details

The author's point is the **main idea** of a text. This is what the author wants readers to understand. He or she supports the main idea with **details**. Sometimes a text has more than one main idea. Details are facts and evidence about the topic.

To understand main ideas and details:

1. **Read the text all the way through.**
   This will help you understand what the text is about.
2. **Look at section titles.**
   These can be clues to how the text is organized and can help you understand what each section is mostly about.
3. **Reread the first and last paragraphs in each section.**
   These paragraphs may state the main idea or give you clues about what the main idea is.
4. **Identify key details.**
   Look for important information, facts, or evidence that seem to support the main idea.

Based on the text you just read, work with your class to complete the chart below.

Main Idea	Details
The Saint Lawrence River played a major role in the development of New France.	

Investigate!

Read pages 110–121 in your Research Companion. Use your investigative skills to look for text evidence that tells you about the goals or motivations of the European nations for colonizing the New World. This chart will help you organize your notes.

Main Idea	Details

Think About It

Review your research. Based on the information you have gathered, what do you think European powers wanted most from North America? How did that affect the people who already lived in North America?

Write About It

Write a Story

Write a short story from the point of view of an American Indian or a colonist. Explain who you are, where you come from, and how your life was affected by European colonization of the New World. Use details from the text in your story.

Talk About It

Compare Your Accounts

Work with a partner who has chosen to write from a different point of view. What were the costs of European settlement of North America? What were the benefits?

Connect to the

Compare

Think about the lasting effects of European settlement of North America. How did trade affect the relationship between Europeans and American Indians?

Inquiry Project Notes

ESSENTIAL EQ QUESTION

What Was Life Like for People in New England?

Lesson Outcomes

What Am I Learning?

In this lesson, you're going to use your investigative skills to explore what life was like in New England for settlers and American Indians.

Why Am I Learning It?

Reading and talking about what life was like in New England will help you learn more about how people interacted in colonial times.

How Will I Know That I Learned It?

You will be able to identify the main idea and key details about the challenges facing colonists and American Indians in New England and then write an essay about the two biggest challenges facing those peoples.

COLLABORATE

Talk About It

Look at the Details Who are these people? How are they interacting with each other? How do you know?

HSS.5.3.2, HSS.5.3.3, HSS.5.4.2, HSS.5.4.3, HAS.CS.5

The First Thanksgiving at Plymouth
by Jennie Augusta Brownscombe

1 Inspect

Read Look at the text. What is the purpose of this text?

- **Circle** words you don't know.
- **Underline** clues that tell you about the purpose of the letter.
- **Discuss** why William Hilton wrote this letter. What did he hope his cousin would do?

My Notes

The Bounty of the New World

Colonists like William Hilton faced many hardships on their journey to North America. They traveled for two months on cramped ships across a rough and stormy ocean. They endured disease, hunger, and seasickness. With luck, they were able to build a settlement without encountering more dangers. Often, however, their worst fears became reality when they clashed with American Indians or failed to grow food. Luckily, Hilton managed to make a good start at his new life.

PRIMARY SOURCE

Loving Cousin,

At our arrival in New Plymouth, in New England, we found all our friends and planters in good health, though they were left sick and weak, with very small means; the Indians round about us peaceable and friendly; the country very pleasant and temperate, yielding naturally, of itself, great store of fruits, as vines of divers sorts in great abundance.

There is likewise walnuts, chestnuts, small nuts and plums, with much variety of flowers, roots and herbs, no less pleasant than wholesome and profitable. No place hath more gooseberries and strawberries, nor better. Timber of all sorts you have in England doth cover the land, that affords beasts of divers sorts, and great flocks of turkey, quails, pigeons and partridges; many great lakes abounding with fish, fowl, beavers, and otters.

The sea affords us great plenty of all excellent sorts of sea-fish, as the rivers and isles doth variety of wild fowl of most useful sorts. Mines we find, to our thinking; but neither the goodness nor quality we know. Better grain cannot be than the Indian corn, if we will plant it upon as good ground as a man need desire. We are all freeholders; the rent-day doth not trouble us; and all those good blessings we have, of which and what we list in their seasons for taking.

Our company are, for most part, very religious, honest people; the word of God sincerely taught us every Sabbath; so that I know not any thing a contented mind can here want. I desire your friendly care to send my wife and children to me, where I wish all the friends I have in England; and so I rest

Your loving kinsman,

William Hilton

From Alexander Young's *Chronicles of the Pilgrim Fathers of the Colony of Plymouth, from 1602–1625*. Boston: Charles C. Little and James Brown, 1841.

2 Find Evidence

Reread the statement "We are all freeholders." What is a context clue for the meaning of the word "freeholder"? Why does being a freeholder mean so much to Hilton?

Underline the details that illustrate why this new status is important to Hilton. How does this help you understand why some people made the long and dangerous journey to settle New England?

3 Make Connections

Talk Could a letter like Hilton's have inspired others in England to move to North America? Would it have persuaded you to make such a long journey?

COLLABORATE

TEXT: Hilton, William. William Hinton to his Cousin, November 1621. In Chronicles of the Pilgrim Fathers of the Colony of Plymouth, from 1602-1625, collected by Alexander Young. Boston: C. C. Little and J. Brown, 1841.; PHOTO: McGraw-Hill Education

Explore Main Idea and Details

The **main idea** of a text is what the author most wants readers to know about the topic. The author uses **key details** to support the main idea. Sometimes the main idea is stated in the text, but readers often must infer the main idea from the key details.

To find the main idea and key details:

1. **Read the text all the way through.**
   This will help you understand what the text is about.
2. **Look at section titles.**
   These can be clues to how the text is organized and can help you understand what each section is mostly about.
3. **Reread the first and last paragraphs in each section.**
   These paragraphs may state the main idea or give you clues about what the main idea is.
4. **Identify key details.**
   Look for important information, facts, or evidence that seem to support the main idea.

Based on the text you just read, work with your class to complete the chart below.

Detail
The main idea is that the land they were in was a great place to settle. **Main Idea**

Investigate!

Read pages 122–133 in your Research Companion. Use your investigative skills to look for text evidence that tells you key details and the main idea. Think about the challenges facing the American Indians and the English settlers in New England.

Detail
Detail
Detail
Main Idea

Report Your Findings

Think About It

Review your research. Based on the information you have gathered, what do you think were the two greatest challenges facing New England settlers and American Indians?

Write About It

Write and Cite Evidence

Write an informative essay about the two greatest challenges facing the New England settlers and American Indians. Use facts and details from the text to support your response.

Talk About It

Explain Your Thinking

Tell a partner about your essay. Did you write about the same issues? Do you agree with what your partner chose?

Connect to the

Make Connections

How did the goals of the Pilgrims and the Puritans in settling North America influence future settlers?

ESSENTIAL EQ QUESTION

Inquiry Project Notes

What Shaped Life in the Middle Colonies?

Lesson Outcomes

What Am I Learning?

In this lesson, you're going to use your investigative skills to learn about life in the Middle Colonies—New York, New Jersey, Pennsylvania, and Delaware.

Why Am I Learning It?

Reading and talking about the Middle Colonies will help you better understand colonial times and how the past still affects life in the area today.

How Will I Know That I Learned It?

You will be able to describe important characteristics of the Middle Colonies, the people who lived there, the way they lived, and the similarities and differences between the colonies.

Talk About It

Look at the Details What positive qualities does the painting convey about William Penn and his treaty?

HSS.5.3.2, HSS.5.4.2, HSS.5.4.3, HAS.HI.1

Artist Benjamin West created this painting, *William Penn's Treaty with the Indians,* almost 100 years after the event.

Young Ben Franklin Arrives in Philadelphia

1 Inspect

Read the text from the primary source and the sentences that introduce it. What does the word *autobiography* in the source's title suggest about its content?

- **Circle** words you don't know.
- **Underline** clues that tell you *whom* the text is about, *what* that person did, and *where* and *when* that person did it.
- **Discuss** with a partner what the text shows you about Benjamin Franklin.

My Notes

Benjamin Franklin grew up in Boston, where he was an apprentice in his brother's print shop. Then he argued with his brother when things he wrote got his brother's newspaper in trouble with authorities. So Franklin, who was just seventeen, left Boston for Philadelphia. On the next page is his account of his arrival in Philadelphia in 1723.

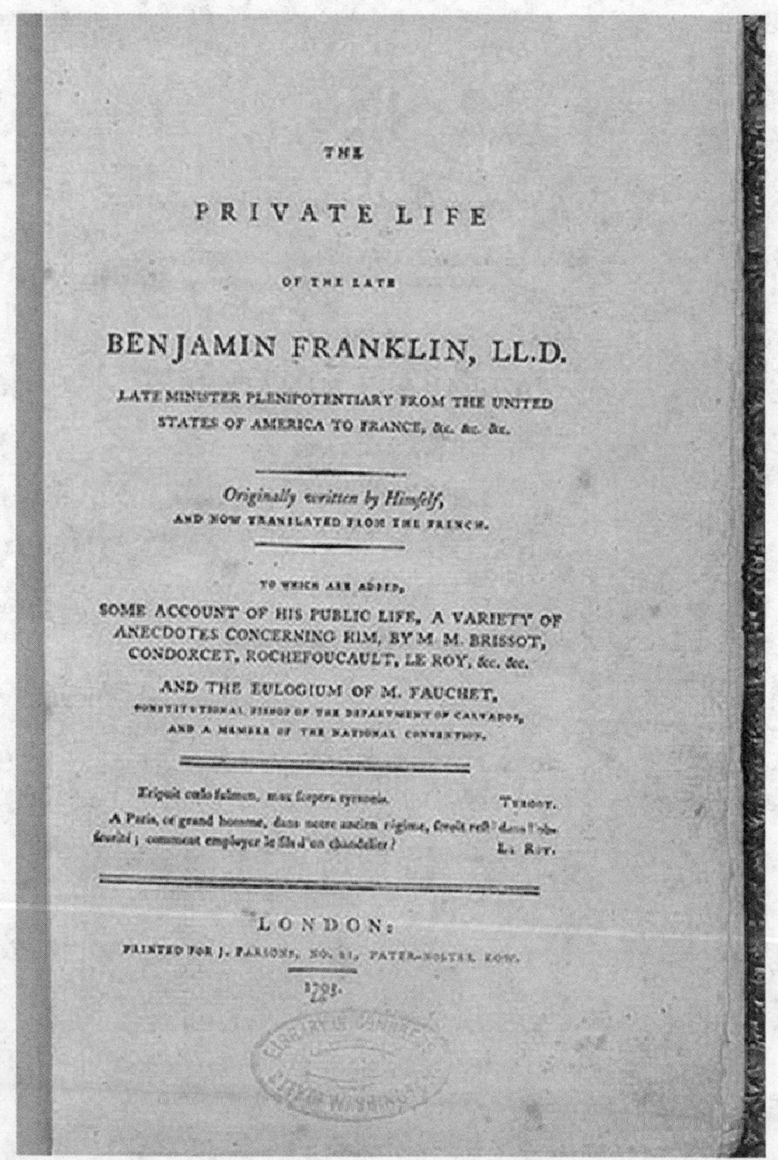

THE

PRIVATE LIFE

OF THE LATE

BENJAMIN FRANKLIN, LL.D.

LATE MINISTER PLENIPOTENTIARY FROM THE UNITED STATES OF AMERICA TO FRANCE, &c. &c. &c.

Originally written by Himself,

AND NOW TRANSLATED FROM THE FRENCH.

TO WHICH ARE ADDED,

SOME ACCOUNT OF HIS PUBLIC LIFE, A VARIETY OF ANECDOTES CONCERNING HIM, BY M M. BRISSOT, CONDORCET, ROCHEFOUCAULT, LE ROY, &c. &c.

AND THE EULOGIUM OF M. FAUCHET,

CONSTITUTIONAL BISHOP OF THE DEPARTMENT OF CALVADOS, AND A MEMBER OF THE NATIONAL CONVENTION.

Eripuit cœlo fulmen, mox sceptra tyrannis. TURGOT.

A Paris, ce grand homme, dans notre ancien régime, seroit resté dans l'obscurité; comment employer le fils d'un chandelier? LE ROY.

LONDON:

PRINTED FOR J. PARSONS, NO. 21, PATER-NOSTER ROW.

1793.

A printed page from Benjamin Franklin's autobiography

PRIMARY SOURCE

In Their Words... Benjamin Franklin

I walked up the street, gazing about till near the market-house I met a boy with bread. I had made many a meal on bread, and, inquiring where he got it, I went immediately to the baker's he directed me to, in Second Street, and asked for biscuit, intending such as we had in Boston; but they, it seems, were not made in Philadelphia. Then I asked for a three-penny loaf, and was told they had none such. So not considering or knowing the difference of money, and the greater cheapness nor the names of his bread, I bade him give me three-penny worth of any sort. He gave me, accordingly, three great puffy rolls. I was surprised at the quantity, but took it, and, having no room in my pockets, walked off with a roll under each arm, and eating the other. . . .

Thus refreshed, I walked again up the street, which by this time had many clean-dressed people in it, who were all walking the same way. I joined them, and thereby was led into the great meeting-house of the Quakers near the market. I sat down among them, and, after looking round awhile and hearing nothing said, being very drowsy through labor and want of rest the preceding night, I fell fast asleep, and continued so till the meeting broke up, when one was kind enough to rouse me.
This was, therefore, the first house I was in, or slept in, in Philadelphia.

—from *The Autobiography of Benjamin Franklin*

2 Find Evidence

Reread the text from Franklin's autobiography. What first impression does Philadelphia make on Ben Franklin? Cite details to support your answer.

3 Make Connections

Talk Discuss with a partner the things you learn about colonial Philadelphia from reading the text from Franklin's autobiography.

COLLABORATE

TEXT: Franklin, Benjamin. The Autobiography of Benjamin Franklin. Edited by Frank Woodworth Pine. New York: Henry Holt and Company, 1916.; PHOTO: McGraw-Hill Education

Inquiry Tools

Explore Compare and Contrast

You can better understand the ideas in a text if you compare and contrast the details the author provides.

1. **Read the text once all the way through.**
   This will help you understand what the text is about.
2. **Look at the section titles to see how the text is organized.**
   Do the titles offer any clues about which important qualities or characteristics are discussed in the text?
3. **Think about what the author wants you to know.**
   When you **compare** two things, you tell how they are the same. When you **contrast** things, you tell how they are different. Consider what the author wants you to know about similarities and differences between colonial Pennsylvania and New York?
4. **Find specific similarities and differences.**
   While reading, ask yourself in what specific ways colonial New York and Pennsylvania were alike. Then ask yourself in what specific ways they were different.

Based on the primary source you just read, work as a class to compare Philadelphia and Boston. List one similarity and one difference in the Venn diagram below.

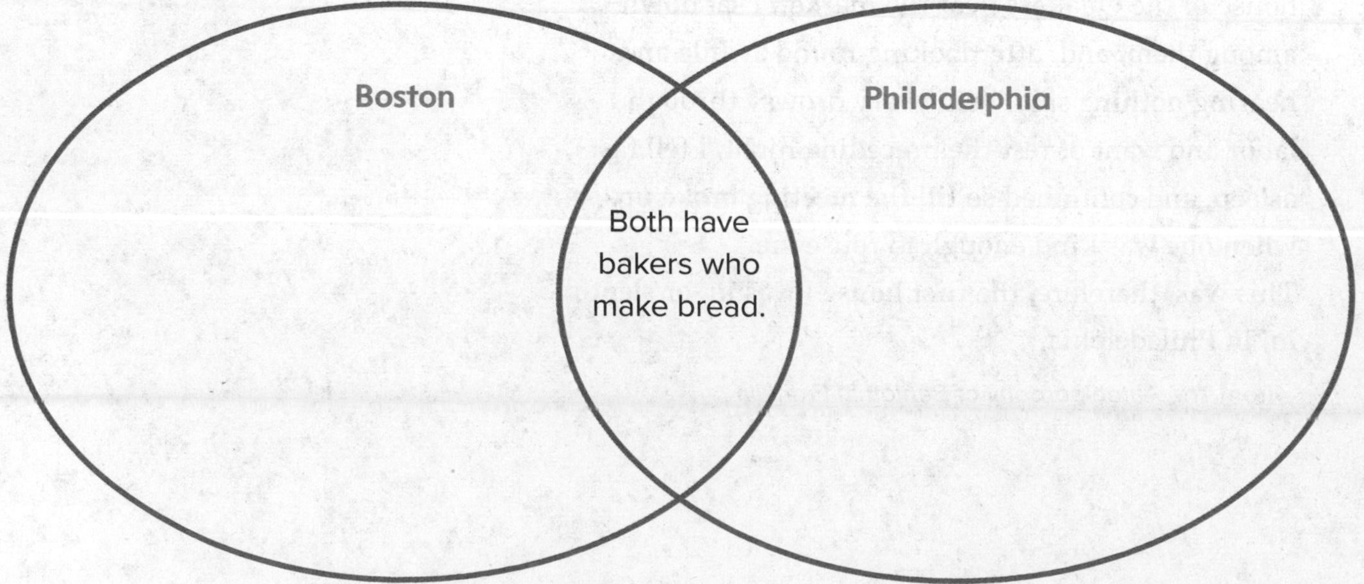

Investigate!

Read pages 134–143. Then add details to the Venn diagram about the similarities and differences between the New York and Pennsylvania colonies. Add at least five similarities and six differences (three for each colony).

Comparing and Contrasting New York and Pennsylvania

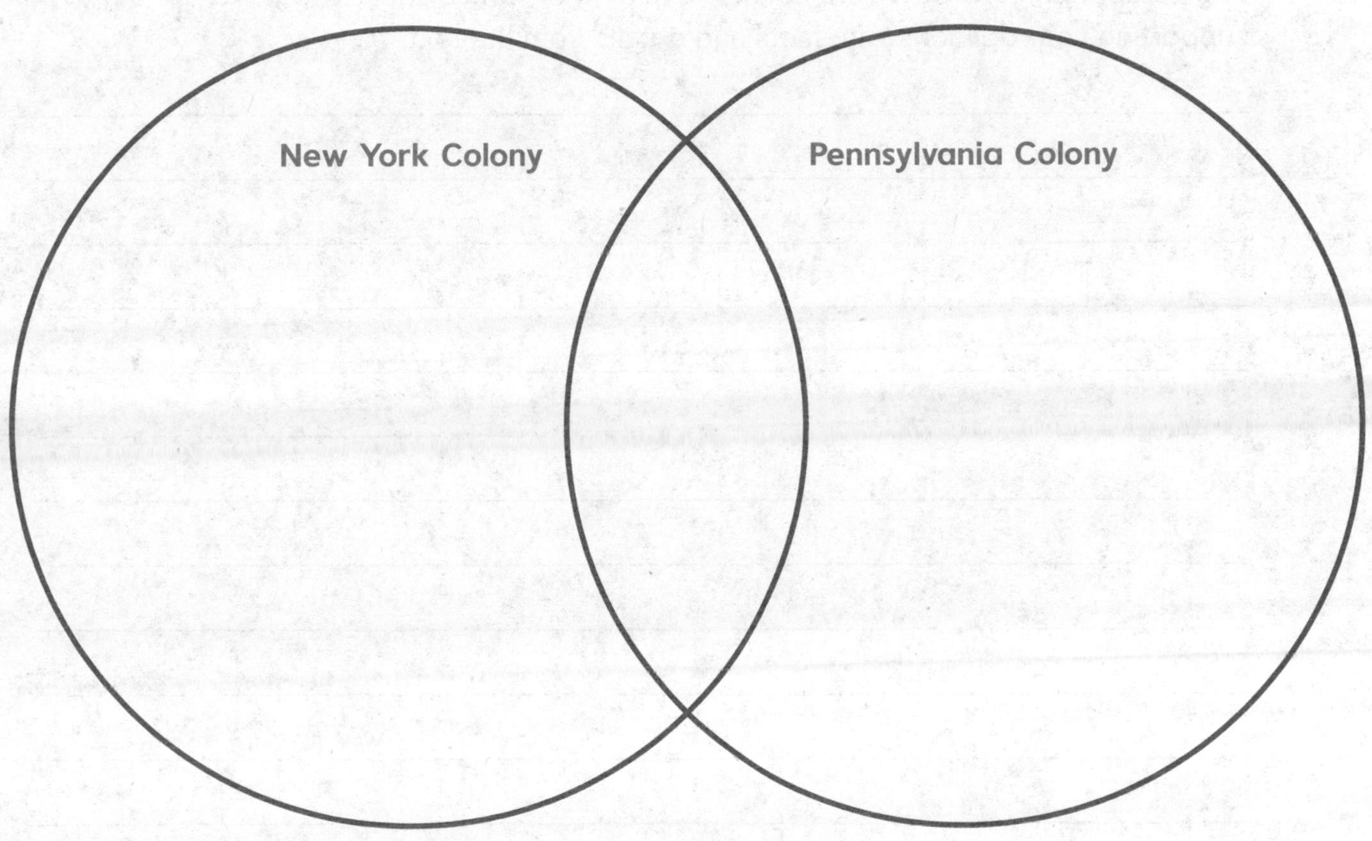

Report Your Findings

Think About It

Review your research. Based on the information you have gathered, how was life in Pennsylvania similar to life in New York? How was it different?

Write About It

Write an Essay

Would you rather be a Quaker settler in the Pennsylvania colony or an English settler in the New York colony? Explain your preference, supporting your opinions with facts and details from the text.

Talk About It 

Defend Your Claim

Work with a partner who preferred to live in a different colony. Discuss the reasons for your preference. Did your partner make any good points that might change your mind?

Connect to the 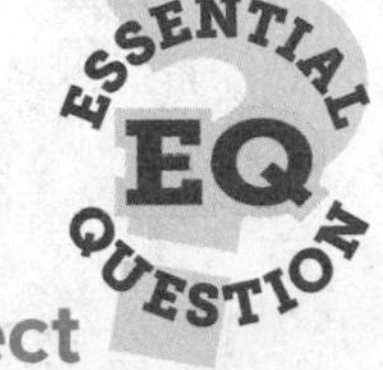

Consider Cause and Effect

Think about the diversity of ethnic backgrounds, religions, and economic opportunities in the Middle Colonies. How did the diversity affect life in these colonies?

ESSENTIAL EQ QUESTION

Inquiry Project Notes

How Did Economics Impact People in the Southern Colonies?

Lesson Outcomes

What Am I Learning?

In this lesson, you're going to use your investigative skills to explore how the economy of the Southern Colonies shaped people's lives.

Why Am I Learning It?

Reading and talking about the lives of people in the Southern Colonies will help you understand how the economy shaped their lives.

How Will I Know That I Learned It?

You will be able to summarize and describe the economy of the Southern Colonies, explain how this economy led to the rise of slavery, and support your explanation with facts and details from the text.

Talk About It

Look at the Details What does this cross-section of a British slave ship tell you about the conditions of the passage from Africa to the New World for African slaves?

HSS.5.3.2, HSS.5.4.2, HSS.5.4.3, HSS.5.4.6, HAS.HR.2

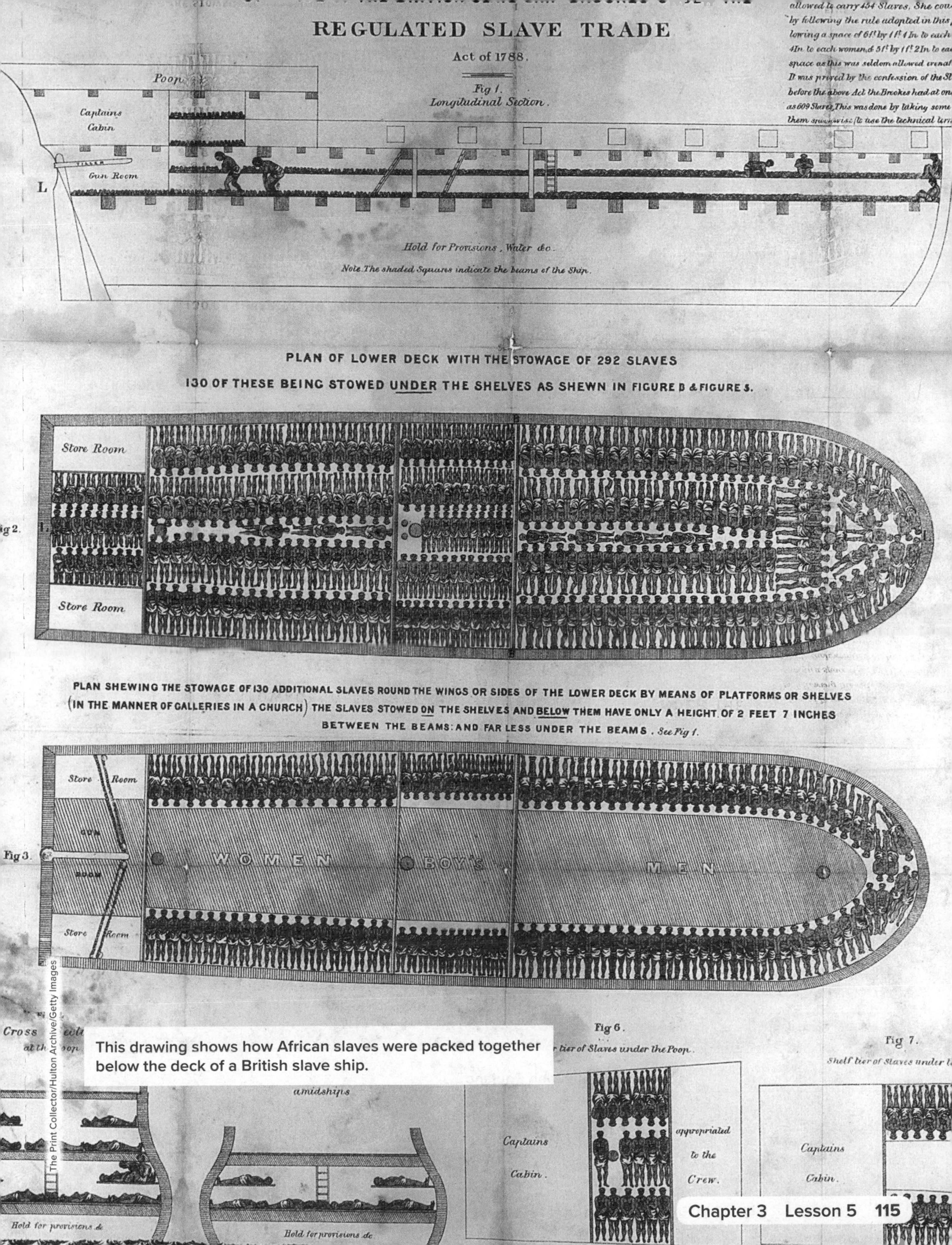

This drawing shows how African slaves were packed together below the deck of a British slave ship.

Analyze the Source

Olaudah Equiano's Account of Life as a Slave

1 Inspect

Read Look at the title. What will the text be about?

- **Circle** words you don't know.
- **Underline** clues that help answer the questions Who, What, Where, When, or Why.
- **Discuss** with a partner what you know about slavery in colonial America.

My Notes

One of the most detailed accounts of life as a slave was written by Olaudah Equiano in the 1700s. His autobiography provides important information about the slave trade and the experiences of African slaves. Equiano wrote that he was born in what is now the West African nation of Benin. When he was 11, slave traders kidnapped him. His account of traveling from Africa to the West Indies on a slave ship is a horrifying description of the brutal treatment of slaves. In the following excerpt, Equiano describes an experience on a Virginia plantation.

Olaudah Equiano

PRIMARY SOURCE

In Their Words... Olaudah Equiano

I was a few weeks weeding grass, and gathering stones in a plantation; and at last all my companions were distributed different ways, and only myself was left. I was now exceedingly miserable, and thought myself worse off than any of the rest of my companions; for they could talk to each other, but I had no person to speak to that I could understand. In this state, I was constantly grieving and pining, and wishing for death rather than anything else. While I was in this plantation, the gentleman, to whom I suppose the estate belonged, being unwell, I was one day sent for to his dwelling-house to fan him; when I came into the room where he was I was very much affrighted at some things I saw, and the more so as I had seen a black woman slave as I came through the house, who was cooking the dinner, and the poor creature was cruelly loaded with various kinds of iron machines; she had one particularly on her head, which locked her mouth so fast that she could scarcely speak and could not eat nor drink. I was much astonished and shocked at this contrivance, which I afterwards learned was called the iron muzzle. Soon after I had a fan put in my hand, to fan the gentleman while he slept; and so I did indeed with great fear.

— from *The Interesting Narrative of the Life of Olaudah Equiano, or Gustavus Vass, the African*

TEXT: Equiano, Olaudah. The Life of Olaudah Equiano or Gustavus Vassa, the African. Boston: Isaac Knapp, 1837.; PHOTO: McGraw-Hill Education

2 Find Evidence

Reread In the Primary Source quotation, Olaudah Equiano indicates he was frightened as he was fanning the slave owner. Why do you think this was?

Reread the statement "at last all my companions were distributed different ways, and only myself was left." What does the word *distributed* mean? Name a word that has the same meaning as *distributed*.

3 Make Connections

COLLABORATE

Write Think about what Olaudah Equiano describes in the Primary Source quotation. Then write a paragraph explaining why you think the colonists would force other human beings to live in the kinds of circumstances described.

Inquiry Tools

Explore Cause and Effect

Some of the events you will read about in this lesson have cause-and-effect relationships. To better understand history, it is important to know about cause and effect. The **causes** of historical events explain why things happened, and the **effects** of the events show why the events are important to people afterwards.

1. **Look for transitional words related to causes and effects.**
   Because, therefore, as a result, in order to, and similar transitional words and phrases can indicate cause-and-effect relationships.
2. **Take note of chronology.**
   Texts will often present cause-and-effect relationships in the order that they happen. This is not always true, though, so be careful.
3. **Analyze the events.**
   Would an event have happened without this particular cause? Would the effect have been the same if the earlier event had never happened? Ask yourself questions like these to determine how strong the relationship between two events is.
4. **Note that an event may have more than one cause or effect.**
   There are usually multiple causes for a historical event. Similarly, a historical event may impact many future events.

Based on the text you just read, work with your class to complete the chart below.

Cause		Effect
Equiano saw an enslaved woman wearing an iron muzzle.	→	

Investigate!

Read pages 144–155 in your Research Companion. Use your investigative skills to identify events and circumstances that led to the growth of slavery in the Southern Colonies.

Cause		Effect
	→	
	→	
	→	

Report Your Findings

Think About It

Review your research. Based on the information you have gathered, how did the way of life in the Southern Colonies lead to the rise of slavery?

Write About It

Explain What Happened

In your own words, write a summary of how the economy of the Southern Colonies led to the rise of slavery. Use facts and details from the text in your summary. What was the human cost of slavery? How could slavery have been avoided in the Southern economy?

Talk About It 

Share Your Thinking

Exchange summaries with a partner. Compare and contrast your explanations of how the economy of the Southern Colonies led to slavery. What did your partner include that you did not?

Connect to the 

Pull It Together

What positive and negative effects did European settlements have on North America and the people living there?

Inquiry Project Notes

Project Wrap-Up

Now's the time for you and your classmates to present your narratives. Here's what to do.

Use your notes to present on the European settlement you chose.

- ☐ Work with your group to read the narrative aloud.
- ☐ Assign each group member to read a character's dialogue or to take on the role of narrator.
- ☐ Read the narrative aloud for your class. Be prepared to take questions from your audience after your performance.

Tips for Presenting

Remember these tips when you present to your class.

- ☐ Help your group members understand how to read their parts and why their characters are important to the story.
- ☐ Encourage your classmates to speak slowly and clearly so the important details of your narrative are easy to understand.
- ☐ Listen carefully to any questions from your audience and answer them using details from the text. If you do not know an answer, explain that you will do research to locate it.

Project Rubric

Use these questions to help evaluate your project.

	Yes	No
Did I include relevant facts and details about the settlement in the narrative?		
Did the dialogue and descriptions I wrote help make the information clear and entertaining?		
Did I fairly show the sides of both the settlers and the American Indians?		
Did I help my group members understand how I wanted them to perform my narrative?		
Did my audience understand what my narrative was about?		

Project Reflection

Think about your work during this chapter. What did you learn? What do you want to learn more about? What could you do differently in the next chapter?

____

____

____

____

____

____

____

Reader's Theater

This Is What I Believe

CHARACTERS

Narrator	General Court Judge 1	Mary Williams
Anne Hutchinson	General Court Judge 2	James Madsen
Governor John Winthrop	General Court Judge 3	Townspeople

Narrator: In 1634, when Anne Hutchinson and her family arrived in Boston, a Puritan woman's jobs were to raise children, keep the household, and obey her husband. Anne Hutchinson, however, believed that she should be allowed to preach to other Puritans. She also believed that Puritanism was too strict.

As the local midwife, she became popular with many women. A group of them often came to hear Anne preach and discuss the Bible with them. Soon, men were coming to these meetings too. Before long, however, male church leaders learned about what Anne was doing. After she refused to stop preaching, they held a trial to decide what to do with her.

(The scene opens on a courtroom. The crowd is noisy. The men sit on one side of the room, and the women sit on the other side. Three judges—the general court—oversee the hearing. Anne Hutchinson *sits in a chair by herself.* Governor Winthrop *stands to quiet the crowd.)*

Governor John Winthrop: Order! Order in the court! *(The crowd quiets down.)*

Judge 1: We are here today to hear the case of this woman, Anne Marbury Hutchinson.

Judge 2: She is accused of heresy.

Judge 3: First, we will hear from Mary Williams, a follower of Hutchinson. Mrs. Williams, please take the stand.

(Mary Williams *rises and stands next to the judges.)*

North Wind Picture Archives/Alamy

John Winthrop: Mrs. Williams, you have been a member of Mrs. Hutchinson's congregation, haven't you?

Mary Williams: Yes, Governor Winthrop. After Anne helped with my baby, we got to talking about this and that.

Before long, we were discussing the church and how women don't have much of a voice in it, even though we have plenty of good ideas.

Winthrop: *(getting agitated)* And during this time, were you reminded of the teachings of our religion? Of the sacred covenant you signed with the church?

Williams: Well, yes, of course, sir. But what Anne said about women voicing their opinions and their beliefs made sense, sir! It's not fair that all the rules should be handed down by men, and we womenfolk are just expected to follow!

(The crowd grows very noisy; this is a shocking statement.)

Winthrop: Silence! *(The noise quiets.)* Mrs. Williams, your actions have been thoughtless, and you have set a bad example. Sit down, please, madam!

(Mary Williams *sits down. A few other women near her lean over to talk to her; some pat her on the back.)*

Judge 1: The court will now hear from James Madsen, who also attended Mrs. Hutchinson's meetings. Mr. Madsen!

(James Madsen *gets up and takes his place next to the judges.)*

Judge 2: Mr. Madsen, is it true that you allowed yourself to be *preached to by a woman?* What do you have to say for yourself, sir?

James Madsen: Yes, sir. Mrs. Hutchinson and I had a long talk while she helped nurse my boy Jamie, sir. We talked about how all the morals and rules that are placed upon us are not needed to keep us in God's good graces. Really, our salvation comes from that grace alone, and not from all this hard work we Puritans put ourselves through.

(The crowd grows noisy again; this is a very serious statement against a major belief of the Puritans.)

Winthrop: Mr. Madsen! Do you realize what you have just said, sir? These statements are heresy! For a woman, who is often guided by emotion, to believe this babble is one thing. But you—you are a man, sir! You have no excuse!

(Winthrop *is overcome with anger and disbelief. He sits down, appearing to be thinking very hard.)*

Judge 3: Mr. Madsen, you can sit down. (Madsen *sits down again.)* Our last witness will be Mrs. Anne Hutchinson herself. Madam, this court is giving you the opportunity to defend yourself against these serious accusations. We recommend that you carefully consider what you say.

(Anne Hutchinson *rises from her chair and stands next to the judges.)*

Bettman/Getty Images

Anne Hutchinson: Your honors, thank you for allowing me the opportunity to speak to you today. But for my defense, I'm afraid that I have none. What Mary and James have said is true.

I stand by my beliefs and my opinions. Ever since I was a little girl, my father taught me to speak my mind. I have read and studied the Bible in great detail. I cannot find any reason women should not be allowed to preach to a whole congregation—including to men. I cannot find reasons for some of our stricter laws and rules.

Judge 2: Mrs. Hutchinson, what you are saying is heresy. If you do not retract your statements, this court will have to act. I am afraid, madam, that you will not like the consequences.

Judge 1: Yes! Remember your place!

Anne Hutchinson: *(calmly)* I understand. But to be untrue to myself would be heresy as well, for my ideas come from God. I have had a revelation, and God has shown me that I am right to be called as a preacher. I will not show myself to be cowardly simply to avoid punishment.

I will not change my statement. You must do as you think best.

(The crowd is in disbelief. The noise rises again.)

Winthrop: SILENCE! *(All noise stops.)* This woman dares to commit heresy! She dares to think that she has the right to lead the souls of men and women. She makes the false claim that her desire to preach comes directly from God!

Anne Hutchinson, your sins are mighty indeed. This court sentences you to banishment from the Massachusetts Bay Colony. You and your family and followers must leave and never, ever come back. This court is adjourned!

(Anne Hutchinson *walks out with her head up, smiling to those around her.* Mary Williams *and* James Madsen *follow her. The rest of the crowd is still chattering in disbelief.)*

Narrator: Yes, Anne Hutchinson and her family and followers had to leave their homes because of Anne's beliefs. However, they simply decided to make a new start. They began a colony in what is now the state of Rhode Island. There, they were able to worship according to their own beliefs.

Write About It

Write your own play about Anne Hutchinson, Mary Williams, and James Madsen taking place one year after the trial. In the play, you should convey through dialogue and narration what life is like for Anne and her followers in their new Rhode Island colony. Do additional research on the colony to make your play more convincing and interesting.

The Road to War

Lesson 1
The French and Indian War

Lesson 2
Patriots, Loyalists, and the British

Lesson 3
The Colonists Rebel

Why Would a Nation Want to Become Independent?

In this chapter, you'll read about what led to the American colonists' wanting independence from Great Britain. You'll examine several causes that led to war, and you'll understand the motivations and opinions of important groups of people.

Talk About It

COLLABORATE

Discuss with a partner what questions you have about why the American colonies wanted to be independent from Great Britain. As you research, look for answers to your questions. Let's get started!

My Research Questions

1. ______________________________

____

2. ______________________________

____

3. ______________________________

____

HSS.5.5.1, HAS.HR.2, HAS.HI.4

Inquiry Project

Which Side Will You Choose?

Write an essay from the perspective of a Patriot, Loyalist, African American, or American Indian, outlining his or her reasons for wanting or not wanting a war with Britain. Use evidence from the chapter and outside research. Form small groups that contain multiple perspectives. The group will debate whether the colonies should go to war. Then hold a vote and present your conclusions to the class.

Here's your project checklist.

- ☐ **Analyze** the task. Make sure you understand what you are expected to do.
- ☐ **Choose** to take the perspective of a group discussed in the chapter.
- ☐ **Conduct** research into the group's beliefs and concerns about the question of independence. Take notes.
- ☐ **Use** your notes to write an essay from the perspective of a member of that group.
- ☐ **Work** with a small group to debate the question of independence. After debating, take a vote about what you should do.
- ☐ **Discuss** the outcome of your debate and your election with the class.

Explore Words

Complete this chapter's Word Rater. Write notes as you learn more about each word.

boycott

☐ Know It!
☐ Heard It!
☐ Don't Know It!

My Notes

habitat

☐ Know It!
☐ Heard It!
☐ Don't Know It!

My Notes

imposing

☐ Know It!
☐ Heard It!
☐ Don't Know It!

My Notes

monopoly

☐ Know It!
☐ Heard It!
☐ Don't Know It!

My Notes

musket

☐ Know It!
☐ Heard It!
☐ Don't Know It!

My Notes

outpost

☐ Know It!
☐ Heard It!
☐ Don't Know It!

My Notes

recession

☐ Know It!
☐ Heard It!
☐ Don't Know It!

My Notes

reconcile

☐ Know It!
☐ Heard It!
☐ Don't Know It!

My Notes

repeal

☐ Know It!
☐ Heard It!
☐ Don't Know It!

My Notes

vandalism

☐ Know It!
☐ Heard It!
☐ Don't Know It!

My Notes

What Caused the Conflict between Great Britain, France, and the American Indians?

Lesson Outcomes

What Am I Learning?

In this lesson, you're going to use your investigative skills to examine the different goals of the British, the French, and the American Indian groups in their conflict over North America.

Why Am I Learning It?

Reading and talking about these goals will help you understand how they contributed to the development and outcome of the French and Indian War.

How Will I Know That I Learned It?

You will be able to identify the differences between these goals, make a claim about how these differences influenced the development and outcome of the French and Indian War, and support your opinion with evidence.

COLLABORATE

Talk About It

Look at the Details This is a portrait of George Washington. What details do you see in this painting and what do you think they say about Washington and his life?

HSS.5.3.1, HSS.5.3.3, HSS.5.3.5, HAS.CS.4

George Washington (circa 1779-1781) by Charles Willson Peale

Analyze the Source

1 Inspect

Read Look at the title "Why Were the Iroquois Important to the British?" Which word in the title signals that the text will describe cause and effect?

- **Circle** words that you don't know.
- **Underline** words that give reasons.
- **Discuss** with a partner the reasons why the Iroquois were important to the British.

My Notes

Why Were the Iroquois Important to the British?

The Iroquois were a powerful confederacy of five (later six) American Indian groups whose homeland was in what is now the state of New York. During the 1600s and early 1700s, the Iroquois dominated the Northeast and Great Lakes regions. Because of this strength, the Iroquois were very important to the British in the French and Indian War. As a result, the British government gave a colonial official, Sir William Johnson, the job of keeping friendly relations between the Iroquois and British settlers.

The Iroquois became British allies because of French policy. When French settlers arrived in North America, they decided to aid the Algonquin and Huron in their struggles with their traditional enemy, the Iroquois. One effect of this policy was that the French strengthened their control over the fur trade. Another effect was that the Iroquois sided with the British against Britain's enemies, the French.

PRIMARY SOURCE

In Their Words...

Sir William Johnson

Such was the prowess of the Five Nations' Confederacy, that had they been properly supported by us, they would have long since put a period to the Colony of Canada, which alone they were near effecting in the year 1688. Since that time, they have admitted the Tuscaroras from the Southward, beyond Oneida, and they have ever since formed part of the Confederacy.

—from a letter to the British Board of Trade, November 13, 1763

Johnson, William. Sir W. Johnson to the Board of Trade, 13 November 1768. In The Conspiracy of Pontiac and the Indian War After the Conquest of Canada, vol. 2, by Francis Parkman, app. A. Boston: Little, Brown, and Co., 1898.

Onondaga warriors and British soldiers around a council fire in the 1700s

2 Find Evidence

Reread What did Sir William Johnson mean by the "prowess" of the Iroquois? Why did this quality make them important to the British?

What policy did Johnson want the British government to adopt toward the Iroquois? What effect did he expect from this policy?

3 Make Connections

Talk Discuss with a partner why France's policy toward the American Indians both helped and hurt the French.

Explore Cause and Effect

A *cause* is a reason why something happens. An outcome or result is called an *effect*. Identifying cause-and-effect relationships will help you understand historical events.

1. **Read the text once, all the way through.**
   This will help you understand what the text is about.
2. **Look for words and phrases that signal cause-and-effect relationships.**
   Such signal words and phrases include *cause, effect, because, so, caused, resulted, as a result,* and *due to*.
3. **Identify the events that are linked by such signal words.**
   Be sure you have correctly identified which event is the cause and which is the effect.
4. **Be aware that a cause can have more than one effect, and an effect can have more than one cause.**
   Notice any cases in which more than one cause or effect is indicated.

Based on the text you just read, work with your class to complete the chart below. Use the text you just read.

Cause		Effect
Sir William Johnson stays on friendly terms with Iroquois.	→	

Investigate!

Read pages 168–177 in your Research Companion. Use your investigative skills to identify cause-and-effect relationships among the events of the French and Indian War. Use the chart to organize the information.

Cause		Effect
	→	
	→	
	→	
	→	

Think About It

Review your research. Based on the information you have gathered, which event do you think was the most important cause of the conflict between the British, the French, and the American Indians?

Write About It

Take a Stand

Write and Cite Evidence In your opinion, what was the most important event in the French and Indian War? What were its causes and effects? List three reasons that support your opinion. Include page references.

Talk About It 

Defend Your Claim

Talk to a classmate who chose a different event. Take turns discussing your opinions and supporting evidence. Do you agree or disagree with your partner's opinion?

Connect to the 

Pull It Together

Think about what you have learned about the experiences of the American colonists before, during, and after the French and Indian War. How might these experiences have begun to change how they viewed themselves as citizens?

ESSENTIAL EQ QUESTION

Inquiry Project Notes

What Were the Views of the Patriots, Loyalists, and the British?

Lesson Outcomes

What Am I Learning?

In this lesson, you're going to use your investigative skills to explore British tax policies and the views of Patriots, Loyalists, and the British.

Why Am I Learning It?

Reading and talking about these events will help you understand economic and political issues that led to the American Revolution.

How Will I Know That I Learned It?

You will be able to identify the arguments and reasoning of Patriots, Loyalists, and the British, choose one side to defend, and support your argument with evidence from the text.

Talk About It

Look at the Details Each of the men on page 141 came from a different background and had his own views. Whom do you think was in favor of independence?

HSS.5.4.5, HSS.5.4.7, HSS.5.5.1, HSS.5.5.4, HAS.HI.4

Thomas Paine (top left), George Mason (top right), Joseph Galloway (bottom left), and John Dickinson (bottom right)

Analyze the Source

1 Inspect

Read Look at the title. What does the title suggest the passage will be about?

- **Circle** any unfamiliar words.
- **Underline** clues about what led to the Stamp Act and what happened after the act was passed.
- **Discuss** with a partner why Edmund Burke criticized the way Parliament ruled the colonies.

My Notes

Edmund Burke Blames Parliament

After the French and Indian War, Great Britain struggled with debt. To help pay for it, King George III and British leaders decided to raise taxes on the colonies. They argued that the colonists should help pay for the troops sent to protect them during the war. In 1765, the British government passed the Stamp Act. It was one of several laws that caused outrage in the colonies.

The Stamp Act required colonists to buy stamps and place them on all printed documents, from newspapers to playing cards. Colonists immediately protested. They called the act unlawful and argued that only elected colonial officials had the power to tax goods.

Colonists were not the only critics of the Stamp Act. A respected member of Parliament, Edmund Burke, spoke on the issue several times before Parliament. He argued that the act was passed in poor judgment. He criticized the British government's strict colonial laws and its refusal to work cooperatively with the colonies. Britain could not just ignore the colonists' complaints, Burke argued. Although he believed that Parliament had the right to tax the colonists, Burke felt that this authority should be used only as a last resort.

PRIMARY SOURCE

In Their Words... Edmund Burke

Never was so critical a measure pursued with so little provision against its necessary consequences. As if all common prudence had abandoned the ministers, and as if they meant to plunge themselves and us headlong into that gulf which stood gaping before them, by giving a year's notice of the project of their stamp act, they allowed time for all the discontents of that country to fester and come to a head, and for all the arrangements which factious men could make towards an opposition to the law.

—from "Observations on a Late State of the Nation," 1769

Edmund Burke speaking before the British Parliament

2 Find Evidence

Reread Note the words "never," "so little," and "abandoned." What do they reveal about Edmund Burke's attitude toward Parliament?

Reread this part of the second sentence: "as if they meant to plunge themselves and us headlong into that gulf which stood gaping before them." What image does Burke create by referring to a gaping gulf and using the word *fester*?

3 Make Connections

COLLABORATE

Write Summarize Edmund Burke's key reasons for blaming Parliament for unrest in the colonies.

TEXT: Burke, Edmund. Observations on a Late State of the Nation. Dublin: Printed for A. Leathly, J. Exshaw, B. Grierson, and J. Williams, 1769.; PHOTO: (t)McGraw-Hill Education, (b)Historical Images Archive/Alamy

Explore Compare and Contrast

To compare, look for similarities—things that are alike. To contrast, look for differences—things that are not alike. Comparing and contrasting the points of view of Patriots and Loyalists will help you better understand both sides of the issue.

1. **Read the entire text once.**
   This will help you understand the topic and main idea.
2. **Look at the title and section headings.**
   What clues do they give about the two ideas being compared in the passage?
3. **Identify signal words and phrases.**
   Words like *both*, *likewise*, and *also* signal similarities. Words and phrases like *but*, *yet*, and *on the other hand* signal differences.
4. **Analyze the details.**
   Take a close look at the details signaled by the clue words. How does each detail help you better understand the causes of the American Revolution?

Based on the text you just read, work with your class to fill in the graphic organizer with Edmund Burke's own views and the views he shared with Parliament.

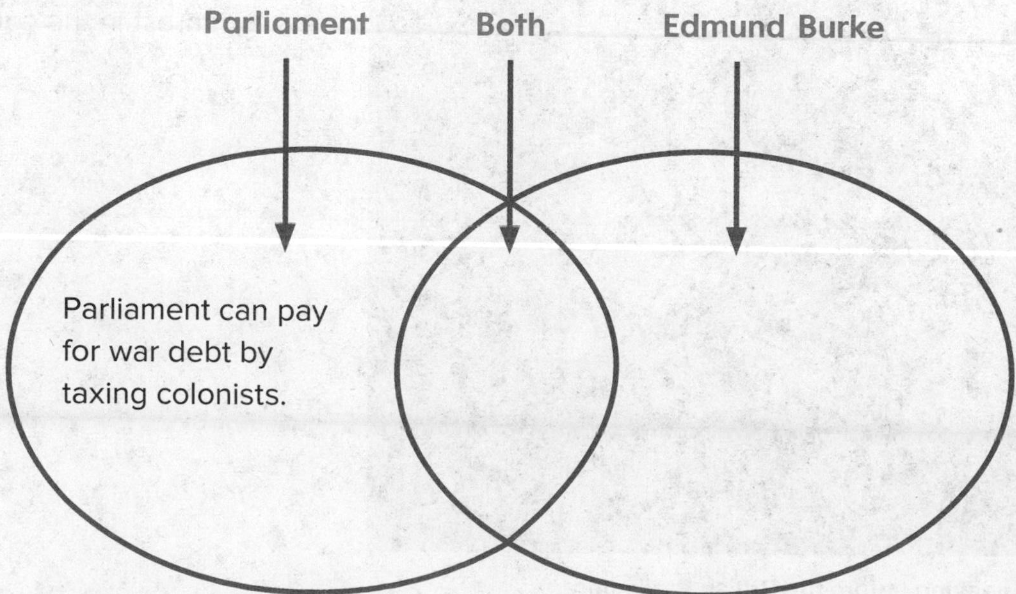

Investigate!

Read pages 178–185 in your Research Companion. Use your investigative skills to compare and contrast the points of view of the Patriots, the Loyalists, and the British.

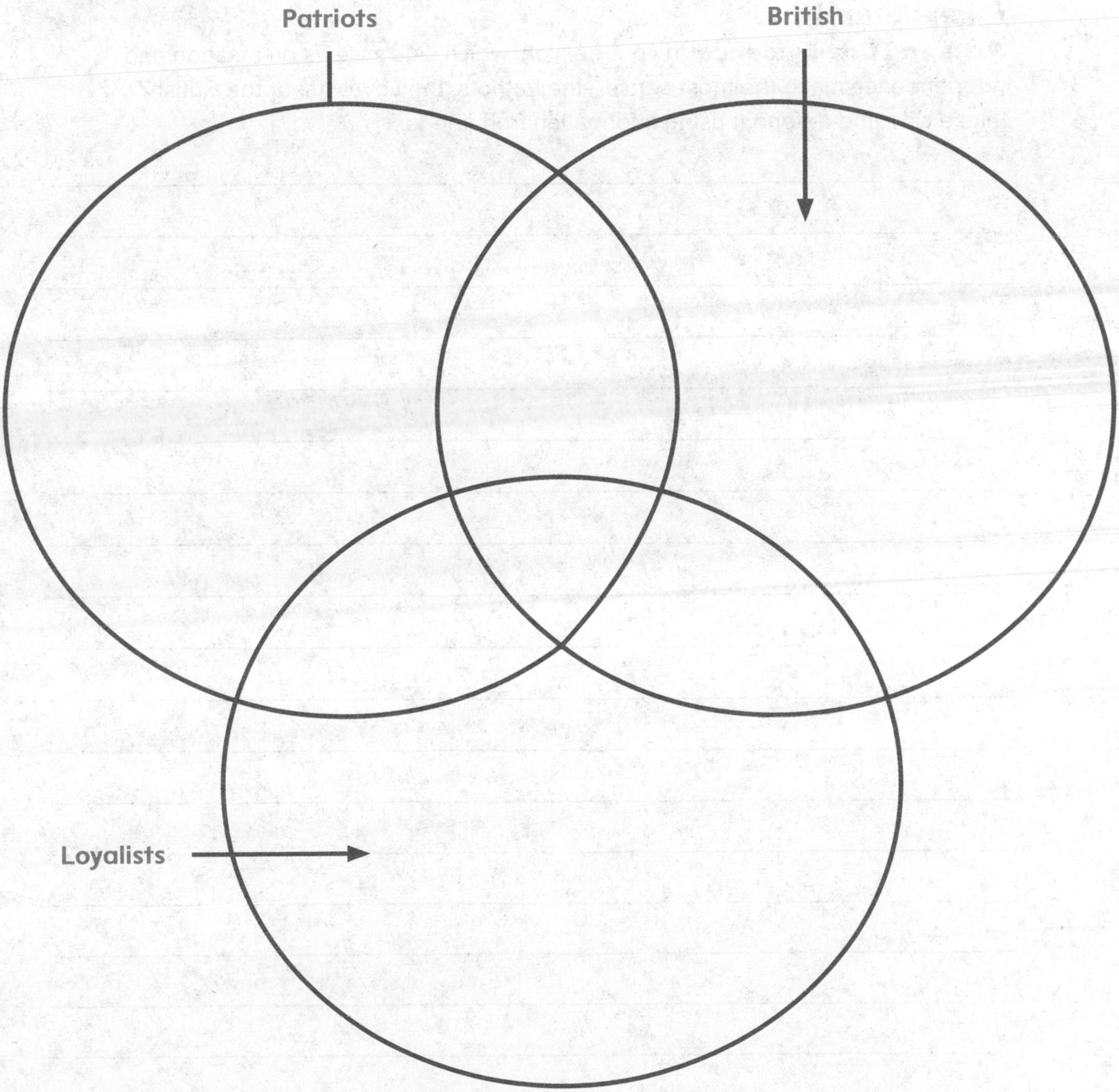

Patriots

British

Loyalists

Think About It

Review your research. Based on the information you have gathered, why did some colonists want to stay unified with Great Britain? Why did others want independence?

Write About It

Take a Stand

Write and Cite Evidence In your opinion, which side's views on taxation and independence make the most sense—the Patriots, the Loyalists, or the British? Take a side and defend it using information from the text.

Talk About It

Defend Your Claim

Choose a partner who took a different side. Discuss your reasoning. Did your partner make any good points that changed your mind?

Connect to the

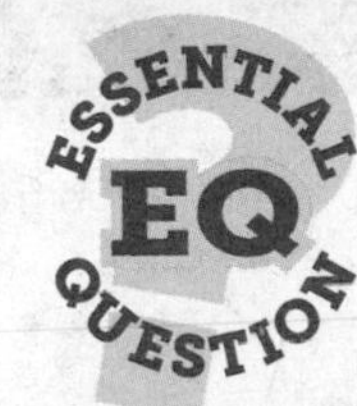

Pull It Together

Why was it so dangerous for Patriots to act on their wishes to have self-government? Why did Great Britain feel the need to keep its hold on the colonies?

ESSENTIAL EQ QUESTION

Inquiry Project Notes

What Increased Tensions Between Great Britain and the Colonists?

Lesson Outcomes

What Am I Learning?

In this lesson, you're going to use your investigative skills to explore events that led to the American Revolution.

Why Am I Learning It?

Reading and talking about these events will help you understand the reasons that many colonists wanted to break free from Great Britain.

How Will I Know That I Learned It?

You will be able to identify the sequence of events that led to the American Revolution, choose the most important event you believe led to the war, and support your analysis with evidence.

Talk About It

Look at the Details What are the differences between the way the British soldiers are portrayed and the way the colonists are portrayed? How do those differences show Revere's point of view of the event?

HSS.5.5.1, HSS.5.5.2, HSS.5.5.4, HAS.CS.1, HAS.HI.3

The Bloody Massacre in King-Street by Paul Revere shows the Boston Massacre from the colonists' point of view.

Analyze the Source

1 Inspect

Read Look at the title of the timeline. What does it tell you about what happens next in American history?

- **Circle** Parliament's actions.
- **Underline** the colonists' actions.
- **Discuss** with a partner the cause-and-effect relationship between Parliament's actions and the colonists' actions.

My Notes

The Events That Led to the Boston Massacre

April 5, 1764 – The Sugar Act

To pay Britain's war debt, Parliament passes the Sugar Act. The act places a colonial tax on imported sugar and molasses. Previous sugar taxes were not enforced. Starting in 1764, colonists who do not pay the tax on sugar products are to be fined and arrested. The colonists stage protests.

March 22, 1765 – The Stamp Act

Parliament passes the Stamp Act, requiring colonists to purchase a stamp for all paper documents, such as newspaper and letters. The money collected from the sale of stamps goes directly to Great Britain, not the colonial government. Colonial protests increase.

May 15, 1765 – The Quartering Act

The Quartering Act is also passed. This requires colonial governments to pay for the housing of British troops and allows the British government to force colonists to let soldiers live on their property, if necessary. No similar law existed in Britain. Colonists call the act unfair.

October 7–25, 1765 – The Stamp Act Congress

Representatives from nine colonies form the Stamp Act Congress. They determine that, since colonists cannot vote in Parliamentary elections, Parliament has no right to tax them. They call for a boycott of British goods.

March 18, 1766 – The Declaratory Act

Parliament declares that it has the right to tax the colonies, but it also repeals the Stamp Act.

June 29, 1767 – The Townshend Acts

Parliament passes The Townshend Acts, adding a tax on goods that are imported from Great Britain. These goods include tea, glass, paper, lead, and paint. Colonists organize another boycott.

August 1, 1768 – The Non-Importation Agreement

Boston merchants declare an official boycott of British goods. They formally refuse to purchase or sell imported tea, paper, glass, or paint until the Townshend Acts are repealed.

October 1, 1768 – The Arrival of British Troops

Parliament sends more British soldiers to Boston to deal with the growing political unrest in the city.

March 5, 1770 – The Boston Massacre

A group of colonists begins to insult a squad of British soldiers and throws snowballs at them. The soldiers fire into the crowd. Five colonists are killed.

2 Find Evidence

Reread Note the year of the first event in the timeline. Then look at the year of the last event in the timeline. How many years do these events span?

Then reread the events in the timeline. Why is it important that so much happened within a short span of time? What does that tell you about the relationship between the colonists and Great Britain at this time in history?

3 Make Connections

COLLABORATE

Talk Discuss with a partner the patterns of behavior in the timeline. What did the colonists usually do in response to Parliament? When did they change their behavior? Why?

Explore Chronology

Thinking about chronology, or the order in which things happen, will help you make connections between related events.

1. **Read the text all the way through.**
   This will help you understand how the text is organized.

2. **Look at section titles.**
   This will give you clues about which events are significant.

3. **Watch for specific dates and signal words.**
   Pay attention to dates and signal words as you read. Words and phrases such as *first, then, within a few months*, and a *few years later* signal the order in which events happen.

4. **Find key facts about each event.**
   As you read about each event, think about what the key facts and details suggest about the growing tensions between the colonists and Great Britain.

Based on the text you just read, work with your class to complete the chart below.

Event	Date	Key Facts
The Sugar Act		

Investigate!

Read pages 186–191 in your Research Companion. Use your investigative skills to identify the sequence of events that led to the American Revolution. Consider how each event is a reaction to another event.

Event	Date	Key Fact

↓

Event	Date	Key Fact

↓

Event	Date	Key Fact

Report Your Findings

Think About It

Review your research. Based on the information you gathered, what was the most important event that led to war with Great Britain?

Write About It

Take a Stand

Write and Cite Evidence Write an opinion essay about the most important event that led to war with Great Britain. What events led up to this moment? What happened as a result of it? Use facts and details from the text to support your opinion.

Talk About It

Defend Your Claim

Choose a partner who wrote about a different event. Discuss the different impacts your events had. Do you agree or disagree with your partner? Why?

History

Connect to the

Pull It Together

How did the growing tension between the colonies and Great Britain eventually lead to war?

Inquiry Project Notes

Project Wrap-Up

Now's the time for you and your group to hold your debate and present your conclusions. Here's what to do.

Use your notes to debate the question of independence from the perspectives of the people you chose.

- ☐ Work with your group to debate the question of independence.
- ☐ Consider why a Patriot's opinion might be different from that of a Loyalist, African American, or American Indian.
- ☐ Take a vote on the issue after the debate.
- ☐ Briefly present your group's conclusions to your whole class. Discuss any similarities and differences in your debates.

Tips for Presenting

Remember these tips during your debate.

- ☐ Be respectful of the points of view of others. Do not interrupt when others are talking.
- ☐ Stay in character. Speak from the perspective of a person in the group you chose.
- ☐ Vote according to the way you think your character would have felt after the debate.

Project Rubric

Use these questions to help evaluate your project.

	Yes	No
Did I choose a side from one of the groups affected by the question of independence?		
Did I research how a member of that group would feel about independence?		
Did I use my research to argue effectively for my opinion during the small-group debate?		
Did I listen carefully during the debate and consider the points of view of the members of my small group?		
Did my group present conclusions about independence to the class in a way that was clear?		

Project Reflection

Think about your work during this chapter. What was the most surprising or interesting thing you learned? What do you want to learn more about? What will you do differently in the future?

The American Revolution

What Does the Revolutionary Era Tell Us About Our Nation Today?

In this chapter, you'll read about the important events and people in the American Revolution. You'll think about why these events and people are important, the impact they had on the Revolution, and how the Revolution still affects our nation today.

Talk About It

COLLABORATE

Discuss with a partner what questions you have about the Revolutionary Era. As you research the people, events, and ideas from the Revolutionary Era, look for answers to your questions. Let's get started!

My Research Questions

1. ______________________________

____

2. ______________________________

____

3. ______________________________

____

HSS.5.6, HAS.CS.1, HAS.CS.3, HAS.HI.1

Inquiry Project

How Would Our Lives Have Been Impacted If . . . ?

You and your classmates will research people, ideas, and events that had an impact during the American Revolution. You will each choose one to develop a timeline card for. You'll evaluate the information in the classroom timeline and choose what you think are the five most important people, ideas, or events. Then you will take one item from the timeline and consider how our country would be different today if it had never happened.

Here's your project checklist.

- ☐ **Analyze** the task. Make sure you know what's expected in each step.
- ☐ **List** important events, people, and ideas from the chapter.
- ☐ **Work** as a group to assign a timeline card to each class member or to small groups.
- ☐ **Assemble** the class timeline.
- ☐ **Choose** what you think are the five most important events on the timeline.
- ☐ **Defend** your choices.

Explore Words

Complete this chapter's Word Rater. Write notes as you learn more about each word.

blockade

☐ Know It!
☐ Heard It!
☐ Don't Know It!

My Notes

inflation

☐ Know It!
☐ Heard It!
☐ Don't Know It!

My Notes

mercenary

☐ Know It!
☐ Heard It!
☐ Don't Know It!

My Notes

militia

☐ Know It!
☐ Heard It!
☐ Don't Know It!

My Notes

monarch

☐ Know It!
☐ Heard It!
☐ Don't Know It!

My Notes

negotiate

☐ Know It!
☐ Heard It!
☐ Don't Know It!

My Notes

---

profiteer

☐ Know It!
☐ Heard It!
☐ Don't Know It!

My Notes

---

rebel

☐ Know It!
☐ Heard It!
☐ Don't Know It!

My Notes

---

reconciliation

☐ Know It!
☐ Heard It!
☐ Don't Know It!

My Notes

---

traitor

☐ Know It!
☐ Heard It!
☐ Don't Know It!

My Notes

How Did the American Revolution Start?

Lesson Outcomes

What Am I Learning?

In this lesson, you're going to use your investigative skills to explore events that happened at the beginning of the American Revolution.

Why Am I Learning It?

Reading and talking about these events will help you understand their impact on the American Revolution and our nation today.

How Will I Know That I Learned It?

You will be able to identify the chronology of events at the start of the American Revolution, state an opinion about which event was most important, and support your opinion with evidence.

COLLABORATE

Talk About It

Look at the Details What do you think is happening? How do you know this happened long ago? What do their dress and appearance tell you about these men?

HSS.5.5.2, HSS.5.5.4, HSS.5.6.1, HAS.CS.4

The Battle at Bunker's Hill drawn by Henry A. Thomas

Patrick Henry Speaks Out

1 Inspect

Read Look at the title. What does "Patrick Henry Speaks Out" suggest about the tone of the text?

- **Circle** words you don't know.
- **Underline** clues that help you answer the questions Who, What, Where, When, or Why.
- **Discuss** with a partner what Patrick Henry thinks the people of Virginia should do and why.

My Notes

In March of 1775, the House of Burgesses met in Richmond, Virginia, to discuss a solution to painful taxes imposed by the British government. The House of Burgesses was an assembly of elected members who represented the settlements and plantations of Virginia.

Several members pleaded for more time to persuade the British government to repeal, or end, the taxes. Finally, a member named Patrick Henry rose to speak. He mentioned the city of Boston, where there had been conflicts between the colonists and the British. He asked what Virginia could do. He went on to say, "We have done everything that could be done to avert the storm which is now coming."

The only possible action left, Henry said, was to take up arms and fight. The House of Burgesses then voted to organize a **militia** for Virginia.

PRIMARY SOURCE

In Their Words... Patrick Henry

Our brethren are already in the field! Why stand we here idle? What is it that gentlemen wish? What would they have? Is life so dear, or peace so sweet, as to be purchased at the price of chains and slavery? Forbid it, Almighty God! I know not what course others may take; but as for me, give me liberty or give me death!

—from "Speech to the Virginia House of Burgesses," March 23, 1775, Richmond, Virginia

Patrick Henry, speaking to the Virginia House of Burgesses, March 23, 1775.

Patrick Henry Addressing the Virginia Assembly

2 Find Evidence

Reread What do you think is the purpose of Patrick Henry's speech? What words does he use that will help accomplish his purpose?

Examine the statement "Our brethren are already in the field! Why stand we here *idle*?" What does the word *idle* mean? Name a word that has the same meaning as *idle*.

3 Make Connections

Talk Discuss with a partner the reasons that Patrick Henry gives for fighting the British.

Connect to Now How did Patrick Henry's speech have an effect on our country today?

Explore Chronology

Identifying the **chronology**, or order in which things happen, in what you read will help you understand how events in history are related.

1. **Read the text once all the way through.**
   This will help you understand what the text is about.

2. **Look at the section titles to see how the text is organized.**
   Do the titles offer any clues as to which important events are discussed in the text?

3. **Watch for specific dates.**
   Are the events described in the text presented in chronological order? It may help to look for sentences that begin with a date—for instance, "On May 10, 1775 . . ."

4. **Find key facts about the events.**
   While reading, ask yourself what key facts about each event show that it was important to the start of the American Revolution.

Based on the text you just read, work with your class to complete the chart below.

Event	Date	Key Facts
Patrick Henry's speech to the House of Burgesses		

Investigate!

Read pages 200–209 in your Research Companion. Use your investigative skills to identify the chronology of events at the start of the American Revolution. Use the chart to organize information.

Event	Date	Key Facts
↓		
↓		

Report Your Findings

Think About It

Take a Stand

Review your research. Based on the information you have gathered, what do you think was the most significant event at the start of the American Revolution?

Write About It

Write and Cite Evidence

In your opinion, what was the most significant event at the start of the American Revolution? List three reasons that support your opinion. Include page references.

Event ______________________________

____

____

Reasons

1. ______________________________

____

____

2. ______________________________

____

____

3. ______________________________

____

____

Talk About It 

Defend Your Claim

Talk to a classmate who chose a different event. Take turns discussing your opinions and supporting evidence. Do you agree or disagree with your partner's opinion? Why?

Connect to the 

Pull It Together

Think about the people and events that you read and talked about in this lesson. How did these help shape our nation today?

____

____

____

____

____

ESSENTIAL EQ QUESTION

Inquiry Project Notes

____

____

____

____

____

____

____

____

Why Is the Declaration of Independence Still Important Today?

Lesson Outcomes

What Am I Learning?

In this lesson, you're going to use your investigative skills to learn about the Declaration of Independence and explore why it is still important today.

Why Am I Learning It?

Reading and talking about the Declaration of Independence will help you learn more about what it means and how it affects your life today.

How Will I Know That I Learned It?

You will be able to explain the reasons for important parts of the Declaration of Independence and recognize the ways they still affect the country today.

Talk About It

Look at the Details How do you think the members of the Second Continental Congress felt after declaring independence from Great Britain? How do the details in this picture support your answer?

HSS.5.5.2, HSS.5.5.3, HSS.5.5.4, HAS.CS.3

The Rebels of '76, or the First Announcement of the Great Declaration

Jefferson's Bold Declaration

1 Inspect

Read Look at the text. What point is the author making?

- **Circle** words you don't know.
- **Underline** clues that help you understand unfamiliar words and concepts.
- **Discuss** with a partner what point the author wants the reader to understand and agree with in this final paragraph.

My Notes

In the final paragraph of the Declaration of Independence, Thomas Jefferson made the most important statements in the entire document. These statements represented the creation of a new nation, the United States of America. The colonists were now on a dangerous path from which it would be difficult to turn back.

PRIMARY SOURCE

In Their Words... the Second Continental Congress

We, therefore, the Representatives of the united States of America, in General Congress, Assembled, appealing to the Supreme Judge of the world for the rectitude of our intentions, do, in the Name, and by Authority of the good People of these Colonies, solemnly publish and declare, That these United Colonies are, and of Right ought to be Free and Independent States; that they are Absolved from all Allegiance to the British Crown, and that all political connection between them and the State of Great Britain, is and ought to be totally dissolved; and that as Free and Independent States, they have full Power to levy War, conclude Peace, contract Alliances, establish Commerce, and to do all other Acts and Things which Independent States may of right do.

—from the Declaration of Independence

The Declaration of Independence, Preamble, July 4, 1776. The U.S. National Archives and Records Administration.

John Trumbull's painting of the writers of the Declaration of Independence presenting their draft to the Second Continental Congress hangs in the United States Capitol Rotunda.

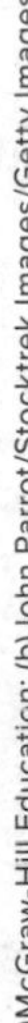

2 Find Evidence

Reread the statement "Absolved from all Allegiance to the British Crown."

Give an example of a word that means the same thing as *absolved*. Then give a word that means the same as *allegiance*. Then explain what the phrase means.

3 Make Connections

Talk Did the 56 men who signed the Declaration of Independence have the authority to separate the colonies from Great Britain? Why or why not?

Explore Cause and Effect

A **cause** is an event that makes something else happen. An **effect** is an event that happens as a result of a cause. Looking for cause-and-effect relationships can help you better understand what you read.

To find the main idea and key details:

1. **Read the text all the way through.**
   This will help you understand what the text is about.

2. **Watch for specific changes.**
   Ask yourself, "What happened?" The answer to this question helps you identify an effect.

3. **Look for explanations.**
   When you have identified an effect, ask yourself, "Why did this happen?" Knowing why something happened will help you explain its cause.

4. **Look for clue words.**
   Words such as *because, therefore, so*, and *as a result* are clues that signal a cause-and-effect relationship. Recognizing these words will help you answer the question "Why did this happen?"

Based on the text you just read, work with your class to complete the chart below.

Cause	Effect
The colonies declare that all political connection between the United States and Great Britain is null and void. →	

Investigate!

Read pages 210–219 in your Research Companion. Use your investigative skills to look for text evidence that tells you how important parts of the Declaration of Independence are still important today.

Cause	Effect
→	
→	
→	

Report Your Findings

Think About It

Review your research. Based on the information you have gathered, what are the important ideas in the Declaration of Independence?

Write About It

Write and Cite Evidence

What was the most important effect of the Declaration of Independence? List reasons that support your opinion.

Talk About It

Support Your Thesis

Talk to a classmate who chose a different effect. Take turns discussing your theses and supporting evidence. Do you agree or disagree with your partner's thesis? Why?

Civics

Connect to the

Make Connections

Which key ideas of the Declaration of Independence remain important today?

ESSENTIAL EQ QUESTION

Inquiry Project Notes

What Were the Defining Moments of the War?

Lesson Outcomes

What Am I Learning?

In this lesson, you're going to use your investigative skills to learn about the defining moments of the Revolutionary War.

Why Am I Learning It?

Reading and talking about the defining moments of the war will help you learn more about how the colonists ultimately won the war.

How Will I Know That I Learned It?

You will be able to make and support inferences about the defining moments of the war.

COLLABORATE

Talk About It

Look at the Details How is Washington shown in this picture? What are his men doing? From the way this portrait was painted, do you think this was an important moment of the war?

HSS.5.6.1, HSS.5.6.2, HSS.5.6.4, HAS.HI.2

John Parrot/Stocktrek Images/Getty Images

Washington Crossing the Delaware by Emanuel Leutze

Analyze the Source

1 Inspect

Read Look at the text. What point is the author making?

- **Circle** words you don't know.
- **Underline** clues that help you understand unfamiliar words and concepts.
- **Discuss** with a partner what the first sentence means: "These are the times that try men's souls." How does that phrase describe what the Revolutionary War was like?

My Notes

Trying Times

From 1776 to 1783, Thomas Paine published a series of sixteen papers called *The American Crisis*. The essays described the conflict with Great Britain as a fight between good and evil.

Paine wrote the first essay in December 1776. During the brutal winter of 1777–1778 at Valley Forge, George Washington ordered that the paper be read aloud to the troops. He hoped that it would inspire them to continue fighting despite the cold, disease, and starvation they faced.

PRIMARY SOURCE

In Their Words... Thomas Paine

These are the times that try men's souls. The summer soldier and the sunshine patriot will, in this crisis, shrink from the service of their country; but he that stands it now, deserves the love and thanks of man and woman. Tyranny, like hell, is not easily conquered; yet we have this consolation with us, that the harder the conflict, the more glorious the triumph. What we obtain too cheap, we esteem too lightly: it is dearness only that gives every thing its value.

—from *The American Crisis*, Number 1.

Paine, Thomas. The American Crisis. London: Carlile, 1819.

American soldiers endured brutal winters during the war.

2 Find Evidence

Reread Examine the statement "the summer soldier and the sunshine patriot will, in the crisis, shrink from the service of their country." What type of people is Paine describing? What other types of people does Paine mention?

Put the phrase "What we obtain too cheap, we esteem too lightly" into your own words. What is Paine saying about the American Revolution with this phrase?

3 Make Connections

Talk What did Paine want to convince the readers of *The American Crisis* to do?

Explore Making Inferences

When you read, you make inferences about the text when the author does not directly state his or her purpose or point. To make a valid inference, you combine **evidence** from the text with what you know from your own experience.

To make an inference:

1. **Read the text all the way through.**
   This will tell you what the text is about.
2. **Reread the text looking for important information - key details, facts, and evidence.**
   Keep track of these clues. They will help you infer.
3. **Ask yourself, *What does the text say?***
   Consider the key ideas the author is telling you.
4. **Then ask yourself, *What do I already know?***
   Connect something you already know with key ideas you have learned from the text to make an observation.

Based on the text you just read, work with your class to complete the chart below.

Text Evidence	What I Know	Inference
Washington had *The American Crisis* read to soldiers during their most challenging time.		

Investigate!

Read pages 220–229 in your Research Companion. Use your investigative skills to look for text evidence that tells you about the defining moments of the Revolutionary War and helps you make inferences about those events.

Text Evidence	What I Know	Inference

Think About It

Review your research. Based on the information you have gathered, why do you think a country as powerful as Great Britain was unable to stop the colonial forces?

Talk About It

Small-Group Discussions

Create a list of reasons that the colonists were able to turn the tide of the war. Read the completed list aloud and decide which two reasons are the most important.

Write About It

News Report

Imagine you are a television reporter covering the Revolutionary War. You must write a report on why the colonies were able to turn the tide of the war.

Connect to the

Make Connections

Think about the qualities that helped the American army turn the tide of the war. How do you see those qualities at work in the United States today?

Inquiry Project Notes

What Was It Like to Live During the American Revolution?

Lesson Outcomes

What Am I Learning?

In this lesson, you're going to use your investigative skills to learn about what life was like during the American Revolution.

Why Am I Learning It?

Reading and talking about life during the American Revolution will help you understand the hardships people faced.

How Will I Know That I Learned It?

You will be able to explore the motivations and understand the people who lived during the American Revolution.

COLLABORATE

Talk About It

Find Details Read the text on the next page. What was life like as a soldier during the American Revolution? What would you have done in Joseph Plumb Martin's place?

HSS.5.6.3, HSS.5.6.4, HAS.HI.4

The Winter at Valley Forge

During the winter of 1777–1778, George Washington's troops camped at Valley Forge in Pennsylvania. The army had great difficulty obtaining enough supplies. Many soldiers became ill, and some died. A Massachusetts private, Joseph Plumb Martin, described his experiences as a soldier in a journal published after the war. The following excerpt describes his time at Valley Forge.

PRIMARY SOURCE

In Their Words...

Joseph Plumb Martin

The men were now exasperated beyond endurance; they could not stand it any longer; they saw no alternative but to starve to death, or break up the army, give up all and go home. This was a hard matter for the soldiers to think upon. They were truly patriotic; they loved their country, and they had already suffered every thing short of death in its cause; and now, after such extreme hardships to give up all, was too much; but to starve to death was too much also. What was to be done? Here was the army starved and naked, and there their country sitting still and expecting the army to do notable things while fainting from sheer starvation.

—from the journal of Joseph Plumb Martin, 1830

A Hopeful Poet

1 Inspect

Read Look at the text. What is the poem about?

- **Circle** words you don't know.
- **Underline** clues that help you understand unfamiliar words and concepts.
- **Discuss** why Wheatley wrote the poem. What does it say about her opinions?

My Notes

Phillis Wheatley was born in Africa. In 1761, at a very young age, she was kidnapped from her family and brought on a slave ship to North America. In Boston, she was purchased by a tailor named John Wheatley. The Wheatleys taught Phillis to read and write, which was an uncommon practice for most slaveholders. She eventually learned Latin and Greek. As a teenager, she began writing poetry. Wheatley composed several of her poems in honor of the new United States. Many of her poems show Wheatley's excitement about the new nation's gaining its independence from Great Britain. That excitement also showed hopefulness for freedom for slaves.

Phillis Wheatley

PRIMARY SOURCE

From "To His Excellency General Washington," by Phillis Wheatley

One century scarce perform'd its destined round,
When Gallic[1] powers Columbia's[2] fury found;
And so may you, whoever dares disgrace
The land of freedom's heaven-defended race!
Fix'd are the eyes of nations on the scales,[3]
For in their hopes Columbia's arm prevails.
Anon Britannia[4] droops the pensive head,
While round increase the rising hills of dead.
Ah! Cruel blindness to Columbia's state!
Lament thy thirst of boundless power too late.

Proceed, great chief, with virtue on thy side,
Thy ev'ry action let the Goddess guide.
A crown, a mansion, and a throne that shine,
With gold unfading, WASHINGTON! Be thine.

1 Gallic powers: Great Britain

2 Columbia: a female symbol of the United States

3 Fix'd are the eyes of nations on the scales: many nations are interested in the outcome of the war

4 Britannia: a female symbol of Great Britain

2 Find Evidence

Reread Examine the line "Proceed, great chief, with virtue on thy side, / Thy ev'ry action let the Goddess guide."

What evidence tells you Wheatley's opinion of Washington? What other evidence in the poem tells you what Wheatley thinks Washington deserves? How might those things conflict with what Washington himself probably thinks he deserves?

3 Make Connections

COLLABORATE

Talk What is Wheatley's opinion of Great Britain? How can you tell from the language she uses in the poem?

TEXT: Wheatley, Phillis. "To His Excellency General Washington." 1775.; PHOTO: McGraw-Hill Education

Explore Motivations

Motivations are the reasons a person does something. When you understand people's motivations for acting a certain way, you learn more about them and the things they did.

1. **Read the text once all the way through.**
   This will help you understand what the text is about.
2. **Ask yourself, *Who is this person, and where did he or she come from?***
   Knowing a person's background will help you understand him or her.
3. **Consider how the person's background influenced what happened.**
   The circumstances of a person's life caused that person to make certain decisions or to act a certain way.
4. **Ask yourself, *How did this person's motivations influence the event?***
   Look for details about the person's motivations or life circumstances that caused him or her to make a decision or to perform some action.

COLLABORATE Based on the text you just read, work with your class to complete the web below by filling out information about a person's background to discover his or her motivation.

Phillis Wheatley was a slave.

Motivation

Investigate!

Read pages 230–237 in your Research Companion. Use your investigative skills to look for text evidence that tells you about the motivations of a person from the lesson. Write the person's motivation in the center circle and details that help explain his or her motivation in the surrounding circles.

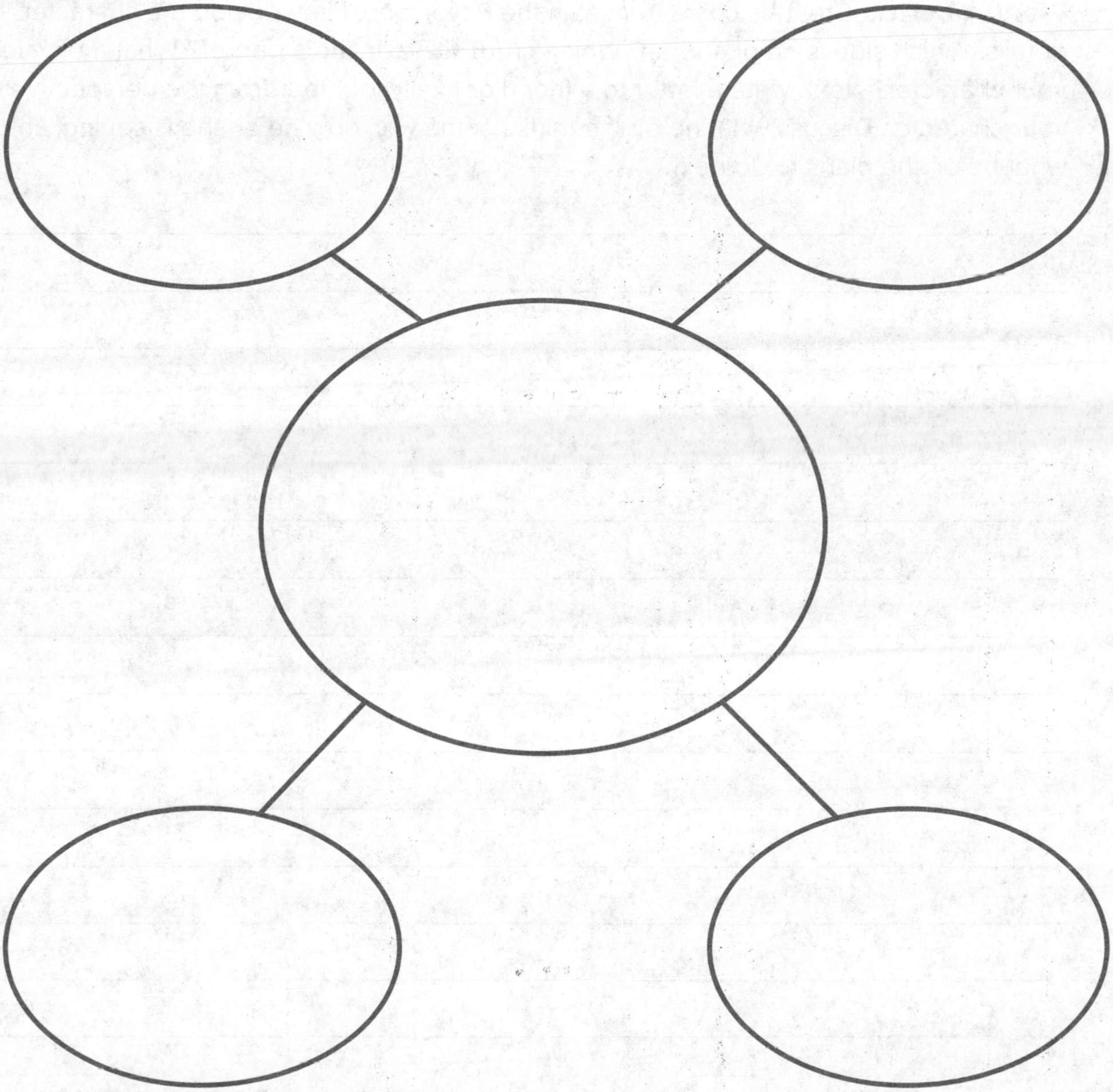

Think About It

Review your research. Consider what you have learned about life during the American Revolution. What risks did people take by fighting?

Write About It

Write a Letter Create a character set in the Revolution. First, decide the character details: Which side is he or she on? Which group is he or she a part of? What motivates your character? Next, write a letter to a friend or family member from the perspective of your character. Discuss what he or she thinks of the war, how he or she is coping, and what he or she plans to do next.

Talk About It

Interview

Work with a partner. Interview each other. One of you will take the role of a journalist, and the other will be the character you created. The journalist should ask questions such as "Why are you fighting / not fighting?" "What do you hope to accomplish?" "How has the war changed your life?" After the first interview, switch roles with your partner.

Connect to the

Make Connections

Think about what you have learned about the American Revolution. What does it have in common with modern conflicts? What is different?

____

____

____

____

____

____

____

____

ESSENTIAL EQ QUESTION

Inquiry Project Notes

____

____

____

____

____

What Did the Colonists Gain by Winning the War?

Lesson Outcomes

What Am I Learning?

In this lesson, you're going to use your investigative skills to learn about what Americans gained by winning the war.

Why Am I Learning It?

Reading and talking about what the American colonists gained will help you understand whether the war was worth fighting.

How Will I Know That I Learned It?

You will be able to understand the causes and effects of winning the war.

Talk About It

Look at the Details How do you think the soldiers on each side of the drawing feel about what is happening?

HSS.5.6.1, HSS.5.6.2, HAS.CS.4, HAS.HI.4

General Cornwallis surrenders at Yorktown.

Washington's Farewell Orders

1 Inspect

Read Look at the text. What is Washington saying about his men's service in the war?

- **Circle** words you don't know.
- **Underline** clues that help you understand unfamiliar words and concepts.
- **Discuss** the terms that show Washington's opinion.

My Notes

Washington gave these final orders to the troops believing that he was about to retire after a long career and return to his home, Mount Vernon, Virginia. He thanked the officers and men. He also reminded them of the good work they had done while fighting for independence. Washington wasn't aware at this time that he would later be asked to serve as the nation's first president.

PRIMARY SOURCE

In Their Words...

George Washington

... Let it be known and remembered, that the reputation of the Federal Armies is established beyond the reach of malevolence; and let a consciousness of their achievements and fame still unite the men, who composed them to honorable actions, under the persuasion that the private virtues of economy, prudence, and industry will not be less amiable in civil life than the more splendid qualities of valor, perseverance, and enterprise were in the field.

—from the Farewell Orders to Continental Army, November 2, 1783

Washington, George. Farewell Orders of General Washington to the Armies of the United States, 2 November 1783. In Monuments of Washington's Patriotism.... Washington, D.C.: P. Force, 1838.

Soldiers listen as General George Washington gives his final orders.

2 Find Evidence

Reread Examine the phrase "let it be known and remembered, that the reputation of the federal Armies is established beyond the reach of malevolence."

What does Washington mean when he says that the army's reputation is "beyond the reach of malevolence"? Use a dictionary to help you define any words that are unfamiliar.

Was this a good phrase to include in his farewell orders? Why or why not?

3 Make Connections

Talk What qualities does Washington say he hopes the men will continue to show in their everyday lives?

Explore Cause and Effect

A **cause** is an event that makes something happen. An **effect** is an event that happens as a result of a cause. Looking for cause-and-effect relationships can help you better understand what you read.

To find the causes and effects:

1. **Look for transitions related to causes and effects.**
   Because, therefore, as a result, in order to, and similar transitional words and phrases can indicate cause-and-effect relationships.

2. **Take note of chronology.**
   Texts will often present cause-and-effect relationships in the order that they happen. This is not always true, though, so be careful.

3. **Analyze the events.**
   Ask yourself, would an event have happened without this particular cause? Would the effect have been the same if the earlier event had never happened?

4. **Note that an event may have more than one cause or effect.**
   There are usually multiple causes for a historical event. Similarly, a historical event may impact many future events.

Based on the text you just read, work with your class to complete the chart below.

Group	Hoped to Gain	Gained or Lost	Results
American soldiers	Hoped for independence from Great Britain		

Investigate!

Read pages 238–247 in your Research Companion. Use your investigative skills to look for text evidence that tells you about what people gained and lost because of their participation in the war.

Group	Hoped to Gain	Gained or Lost	Results

Report Your Findings

Think About It

Review your research. Recall what you have learned about the people involved in the Revolutionary War. What were their justifications for going to war? Did they succeed in their goals or not?

Write About It

Write a Letter Take the role of a representative of one of the groups involved in the American Revolution. This could be a Patriot, a Loyalist, an African American, an American Indian, a member of an ally nation, or even a British soldier. Write a letter to Benjamin Franklin, John Adams, and John Jay about the peace talks in Paris. What conditions would your group like to see included in the peace agreement? Persuade them with specific reasons why your group deserves these conditions.

Talk About It

Defend Your Claims

Discuss as a class who were the real winners and losers of the war. Who got what they wanted? Who didn't? Who lost the most? What was fair and what was unfair?

Connect to the

Make Connections

Think about how the American Revolution ended. What lasting effects did this have on our nation?

____

____

____

____

____

____

____

ESSENTIAL EQ QUESTION

Inquiry Project Notes

____

____

____

____

____

____

____

Project Wrap-Up

Now's the time for you and your classmates to share your opinions about the most important people, ideas, or events from the American Revolution. Here's what to do.

Use the classroom timeline to explain the five most important people, ideas, or events.

- ☐ Talk about how our nation would be different today if one of the timeline items had never happened.
- ☐ Defend your explanation using evidence from your research.
- ☐ Answer questions from others about the points you made.

Tips for Presenting

Remember these tips when you present to your class.

- ☐ Be sure to prepare and practice a couple of times.
- ☐ Speak loudly and clearly.
- ☐ Look your listeners in the eye.
- ☐ Relax and enjoy yourself!

Project Rubric

Use these questions to help evaluate your project.

	Yes	No
Did I identify my top five people, ideas, or events?		
Did I clearly explain how our nation would be different today if one of these had never happened?		
Did I organize the information in a way that best communicates it?		
Did I use words from the Word Bank?		
Was I able to explain the organization to the class?		

Project Reflection

Think about the work you did in this chapter, either with a group or on your own. Describe something that you think you did very well. What is something that you would do differently?

Surviving the Winter at Valley Forge

CHARACTERS

Narrator	Jonathan *(soldier)*	Grandfather
Mother	Father	
Martha *(sister)*	Lawrence *(brother)*	

Narrator: Our play begins in the cold winter of 1778. We visit the home of the Millers, a Patriot family in Concord, Massachusetts. The Millers' oldest son, Jonathan, is an 18-year-old soldier with the Continental Army at Valley Forge in Pennsylvania, under General George Washington's command. The Millers are worried about Jonathan. They have heard that the soldiers at Valley Forge are exhausted and need food and supplies.

The Millers have just received a letter from Jonathan.

Mother: Come here, everyone! Gather around! I have a letter from Jonathan at Valley Forge!

Martha: Is he safe, Mother?

Mother: Yes, thank goodness! Let us read his letter.

Jonathan *(appears, alone on the opposite side of the stage. He is seated as if writing a letter)*:

My Dear Family,

Greetings to you all. I miss you very much, especially you, dear Grandfather! Life here is rather difficult. It has been snowing and raining without end. We sleep in log huts and try to keep warm around the campfires. Many soldiers are ill and some have died. Do not worry, however, for I remain in good health. I am willing to fight for our freedom at any cost.

General Washington is trying to get us more supplies. He is a great man and our victory is in his hands. He has asked for help from a Prussian general named von Steuben. He is teaching us how to march and work together. We'll be a polished fighting force soon, and I know the Patriots will win!

I hope you are well. Please write to me and send me news. Words from you are a great comfort.

Your soldier son and brother,

Jonathan

(Jonathan *exits.)*

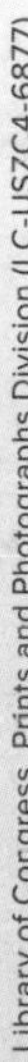

Mother: My poor, brave boy! So young and such a Patriot!

Martha: How can anyone in these colonies support the king?

Father: It is tradition, I suppose. They are Loyalists because they still consider themselves subjects of the British king.

Grandfather: It can be difficult for people to change. Why, when I was a boy, I would never have dreamed of fighting the king! Such a thing would have been impossible to consider.

Father: We Patriots have a grander vision for the future of the colonies. We want the right to form our own government and make our own laws!

Martha: I've heard that there are people who help the British troops by giving them information, shelter, and supplies! Is that true?

Mother: I am afraid that is so, Martha. They call themselves Loyalists because they are loyal to the British crown. But I believe that we will win the war against Great Britain and gain our freedom!

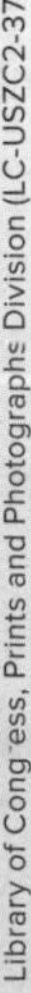
Library of Congress, Prints and Photographs Division (LC-USZC2-3793)

Lawrence: How can you be certain?

Father: Our army is strong and wants to win.

Lawrence: Yes, but the British army is stronger, and I'm sure they want to win too. They also have the support of a king, while my brother and his fellow soldiers freeze without even blankets and food!

Mother: Yes, Lawrence, but our soldiers know the land well and they are loyal to the cause of freedom. They will fight hard to protect their land and their families.

Grandfather: Yes, my dear. Your reasons are good to remember.

Mother: I still worry for Jonathan. I must send him a woolen shirt and blankets to keep him warm.

Father: And we must also write a letter to Jonathan. He can still receive it before General Washington moves his soldiers again.

Martha: I have the ink and the paper. What shall we say?

Narrator: Winter turned to spring, and conditions began to improve at Valley Forge. Food arrived from local farmers. New soldiers arrived. Baron von Steuben's training began to show in the way the soldiers marched and prepared for battle. The Continental Army had suffered at Valley Forge, but it was ready now to return to the battle for its country's freedom.

Write About It

Write your own play about Jonathan and the other soldiers at Valley Forge. Set the play in the spring of 1778. Jonathan has just received a letter from his family. Have the soldiers talk about their concerns in fighting the British. Jot down your ideas in the space below before writing your play.

____

____

____

____

____

____

____

____

Forming a New Government

Lesson 1
The Articles of Confederation

Lesson 2
A New Framework for Governing

Lesson 3
Protecting the Rights of Citizens

How Does the Constitution Help Us Understand What It Means to Be an American?

In this chapter, you'll read about how the U.S. Constitution was created. You'll learn why the Articles of Confederation was too weak to govern the nation, and you'll learn how the Constitution has evolved to protect the rights of all citizens.

Talk About It

COLLABORATE

Discuss with a partner what questions you have about the United States Constitution. As you research, look for answers to your questions. Let's get started!

My Research Questions

1. ____

____

2. ____

____

3. ____

____

HSS.5.7.3, HSS.5.7.4, HAS.HR.2, HAS.HI.4

Inquiry Project

Which Side Will You Choose?

As a class, propose a new amendment to the Constitution that has a good case for and against it. Then, divide into two groups—one in favor of it and one opposed. On a class website, write a series of letters or editorials for and against the amendment, making references to points made in one another's writings.

Here's your project checklist.

- ☐ **Analyze** the task. Make sure you understand what you are expected to do.
- ☐ **Work together** to choose an amendment that could be argued for or against.
- ☐ **Conduct** research into the history and specifics of the topic of the amendment, and think critically with your small group about what it means. Take notes.
- ☐ **Use** your notes to write letters or editorials about the amendment.
- ☐ **Read** the other group's letters, and respond to their claims.
- ☐ **Develop** a written conversation about the amendment.

Explore Words

Complete this chapter's Word Rater. Write notes as you learn more about each word.

amendment My Notes

☐ Know It!
☐ Heard It!
☐ Don't Know It!

article My Notes

☐ Know It!
☐ Heard It!
☐ Don't Know It!

bill My Notes

☐ Know It!
☐ Heard It!
☐ Don't Know It!

currency My Notes

☐ Know It!
☐ Heard It!
☐ Don't Know It!

delegate My Notes

☐ Know It!
☐ Heard It!
☐ Don't Know It!

issue

☐ Know It!
☐ Heard It!
☐ Don't Know It!

My Notes

jury

☐ Know It!
☐ Heard It!
☐ Don't Know It!

My Notes

physical

☐ Know It!
☐ Heard It!
☐ Don't Know It!

My Notes

press

☐ Know It!
☐ Heard It!
☐ Don't Know It!

My Notes

term

☐ Know It!
☐ Heard It!
☐ Don't Know It!

My Notes

What Was the Articles of Confederation and Why Did It Fail?

Lesson Outcomes

What Am I Learning?

In this lesson, you're going to use your investigative skills to explore the Articles of Confederation.

Why Am I Learning It?

Reading and talking about the laws passed in the Articles will help you understand the process that led to the creation of the United States Constitution.

How Will I Know That I Learned It?

You will be able to evaluate the strengths and weaknesses of the first constitutional document of the United States.

Talk About It

Look at the Details How is this image of the Articles of Confederation similar to other important documents from U.S. history? In what ways do you think this document differs from government documents written today?

HSS.5.6.6, HSS.5.7.1, HAS.HR.2, HAS.HI.1, HAS.HI.3

To all to whom these Presents shall come, we the under signed Delegates of the States affixed to our Names send greeting. Whereas the Delegates of the United States of America in Congress assembled did on the fifteenth day of November in the Year of our Lord One Thousand Seven Hundred and Seventy seven, and in the Second Year of the Independence of America agree to certain articles of Confederation and perpetual Union between the States of Newhampshire, Massachusetts-bay, Rhodeisland and Providence Plantations, Connecticut, New York, New Jersey, Pennsylvania, Delaware, Maryland, Virginia, North Carolina, South Carolina and Georgia in the Words following, viz. "Articles of Confederation and perpetual Union between the States of Newhampshire, Massachusetts-bay, Rhodeisland and Providence Plantations, Connecticut, New-York, New-Jersey, Pennsylvania, Delaware, Maryland, Virginia, North-Carolina, South-Carolina and Georgia.

Article I. The Stile of this confederacy shall be "The United States of America."

Article II. Each state retains its sovereignty, freedom and independence, and every Power, Jurisdiction and right, which is not by this confederation expressly delegated to the United States, in Congress assembled.

Article III. The said states hereby severally enter into a firm league of friendship with each other, for their common defence, the security of their Liberties, and their mutual and general welfare, binding themselves to assist each other, against all force offered to, or attacks made upon them, or any of them, on account of religion, sovereignty, trade, or any other pretence whatever.

Article IV. The better to secure and perpetuate mutual friendship and intercourse among the people of the different states in this union, the free inhabitants of each of these states, paupers, vagabonds and fugitives from Justice excepted, shall be entitled to all privileges and immunities of free citizens in the several states; and the people of each state shall have free ingress and regress to and from any other state, and shall enjoy therein all the privileges of trade and commerce, subject to the same duties, impositions and restrictions as the inhabitants thereof respectively, provided that such restriction shall not extend so far as to prevent the removal of property imported into any state, to any other state of which the Owner is an inhabitant; provided also that no imposition, duties or restriction shall be laid by any state, on the property of the united states, or either of them.

If any Person guilty of, or charged with treason, felony, or other high misdemeanor in any state, shall flee from Justice, and be found in any of the united states, he shall upon demand of the Governor or executive power, of the state from which he fled, be delivered up and removed to the state having jurisdiction of his offence.

Full faith and credit shall be given in each of these states to the records, acts and judicial proceedings of the courts and magistrates of every other state.

Article V. For the more convenient management of the general

The Articles of Confederation

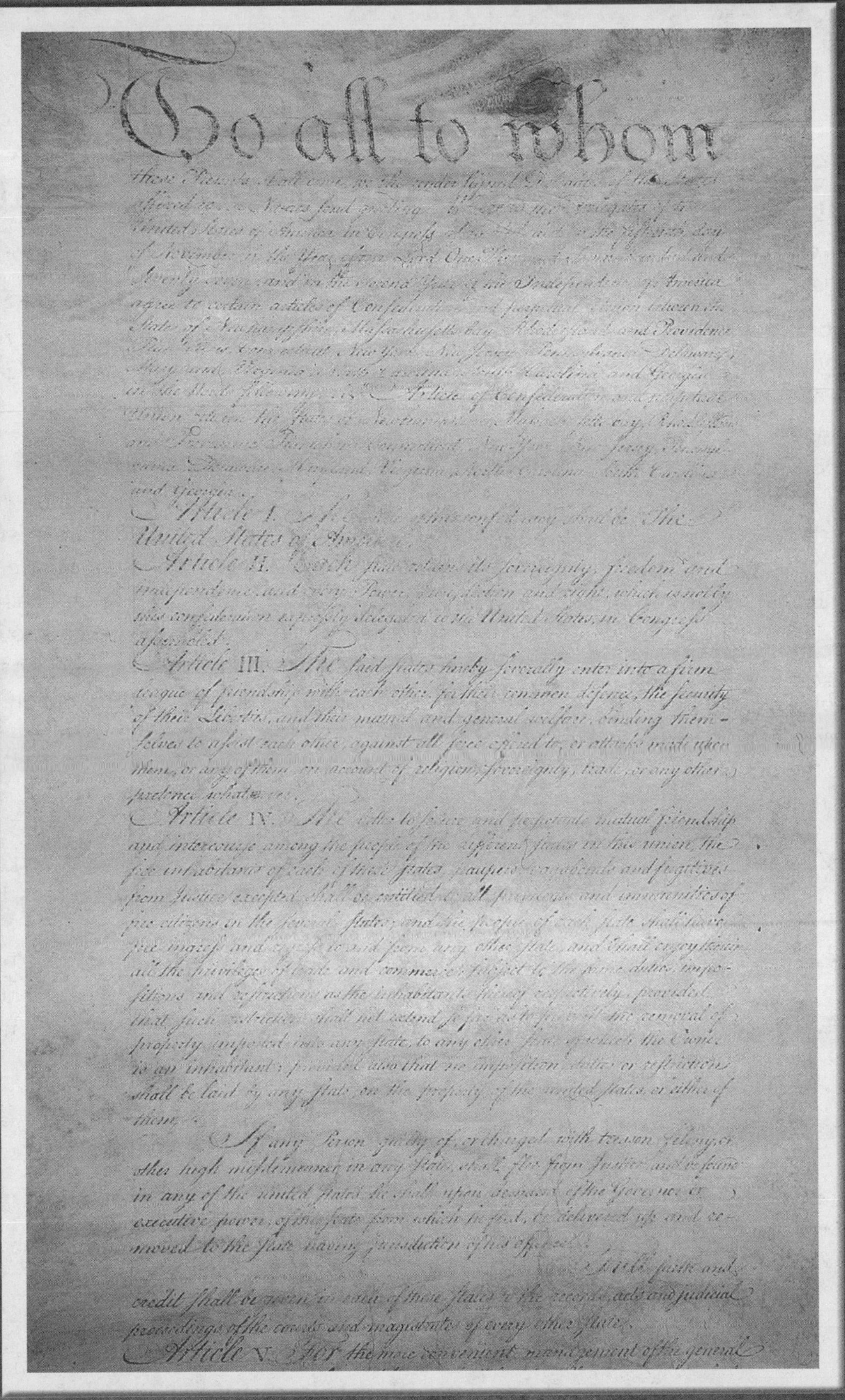

1 Inspect

Read Look at the title. What can you infer about the author(s) of this text?

- **Circle** words you don't know. Look them up and rewrite each article in simpler language.
- **Underline** action words in the articles. What actions do the Articles of Confederation grant the states and Congress?
- **Discuss** with a partner why the writers of the Articles of Confederation might have decided to separate the document into different articles.

My Notes

Excerpts from the Articles of Confederation

Article II.

Each state retains its sovereignty, freedom, and independence, and every power, jurisdiction, and right, which is not by this Confederation expressly delegated to the United States, in Congress assembled.

Article X.

The Committee of the States, or any nine of them, shall be authorized to execute, in the recess of Congress, such of the powers of Congress as the United States in Congress assembled, by the consent of the nine States, shall from time to time think expedient to vest them with; provided that no power be delegated to the said Committee, for the exercise of which, by the Articles of Confederation, the voice of nine States in the Congress of the United States assembled be requisite.

Article XIII.

All bills of credit emitted, monies borrowed, and debts contracted by, or under the authority of Congress, before the assembling of the United States, in pursuance of the present confederation, shall be deemed and considered as a charge against the United States, for payment and satisfaction whereof the said United States, and the public faith are hereby solemnly pledged.

Articles of Confederation, arts. 2, 10, 12. March 1, 1781. Documents Illustrative of the Formation of the Union of the American States. Government Printing Office, 1927. House Document No. 398.

PRIMARY SOURCE

In Their Words...

Alexander Hamilton

But the confederation itself is defective and requires to be altered. It is neither fit for war nor peace. The idea of an uncontrollable sovereignty in each state over its internal police will defeat the other powers given to Congress and make our union feeble and precarious. There are instances without number where acts necessary for the general good, and which rise out of the powers given to Congress, must interfere with the internal police of the states . . .

—from a letter to James Duane, September 2, 1780

TEXT: Hamilton, Alexander. Alexander Hamilton to James Duane, 3 September 1780. Founders Online, National Archives.; PHOTO: (t)McGraw-Hill Education; (b)Library of Congress, Prints and Photographs Division [LC-USZC4-6423]

2 Find Evidence

Reread What weakness of the Articles of Confederation does Alexander Hamilton identify in this letter?

Examine Reread the statement "the idea of an uncontrollable sovereignty in each state over its internal police will defeat the other powers given to Congress and make our union feeble and precarious." Based on this context, what does the word *feeble* mean? Name a word that has the same meaning as *feeble*.

3 Make Connections

Talk Discuss with a partner how the Articles helped set up a central government. Which responsibilities of government did the founders think were most important?

Determine Pros and Cons

Asking questions about what you read will allow you to judge the positive and negative outcomes of historical events.

1. **Read the text all the way through.**
   This will help you understand what the text is about.

2. **Answer *who*, *what*, *where*, and *when*.**
   Write down the dates, places, events, and people mentioned in the text.

3. **Make inferences about the historical reasons for an event.**
   Sometimes the author directly explains how and why something happened; other times, you will have to make inferences. Combine your prior knowledge with what you read in the text to understand the context of the events mentioned in the text.

4. **Identify positive and negative effects.**
   Once you've answered questions about a text, you can use the information to list the pros and cons that resulted from the historical events you've read about.

Based on the text you just read, work with your class to complete the chart below.

Pros	Cons
The Articles give states much freedom to govern themselves.	

Investigate!

Read pages 258–265 in your Research Companion. Use your investigative skills to identify the pros and cons of the Articles of the Confederation.

Pros	Cons

Report Your Findings

Think About It

What were the pros and cons of the Articles of the Confederation?

Write About It

Take a Stand

Write and Cite Evidence Write a short summary of the pros and cons of the Articles of Confederation. How did using this document provide the new nation with lessons about governing?

Talk About It 

Defend Your Claim

Discuss the Articles of Confederation with a partner. Why is it important to learn about the Founding Fathers' mistakes as well as their triumphs?

Civics

Connect to the 

Pull It Together

What would it have meant to be an American citizen if the Articles of Confederation had lasted as the nation's government?

______

______

______

______

______

______

ESSENTIAL EQ QUESTION

Inquiry Project Notes

______

______

______

______

______

______

______

______

How Does the Constitution Set Up Our Government Framework?

Lesson Outcomes

What Am I Learning?

In this lesson, you're going to use your investigative skills to explore the writing of the U.S. Constitution.

Why Am I Learning It?

Reading and talking about the writing of the Constitution will help you understand our government, its laws, and the ideas behind the laws.

How Will I Know That I Learned It?

You will be able to explain the structure of our government and the reasons for this structure.

COLLABORATE

Talk About It

Find Details Read the letter from George Washington to the Secretary for Foreign Affairs, John Jay. How do they feel about the Articles of Confederation?

.7.3, HSS.5.7.4, HAS.HR.2, HAS.HI.3

PRIMARY SOURCE

A Letter to John Jay from George Washington, May 18, 1786

I coincide perfectly in sentiment with you, my dear Sir, that there are errors in our national Government which call for correction; loudly, I would add; but I shall find my self happily mistaken if the remedies are at hand. . . . That it is necessary to revise, and amend the articles of Confederation, I entertain no doubt; but what may be the consequences of such an attempt is doubtful. Yet, something must be done, or the fabrick must fall. It certainly is tottering.

—from *The Writings of George Washington*

Analyze the Source

1 Inspect

Read Look at the two versions of the Preamble to the Constitution.

- **Circle** words you don't know.
- **Underline** phrases that are in both versions.
- **Discuss** in groups of three. Each group member should lead a short discussion for one of the following questions: Why were some things kept? Why were some things removed? Why were some things added?

My Notes

Writing (and Rewriting) the Constitution

The Constitution was not written all at once. It had to be written carefully so that it could cover all of the important laws needed by a national government. On May 25, 1787, fifty-five members of the Constitutional Convention began meeting at Philadelphia's State House to discuss, plan, and write the Constitution.

A first draft was copied and given to the delegates on August 6. They studied and made notes on their copies before making a final draft, signed on September 17, 1787. The Preamble, or introduction, to the Constitution, changed significantly between the two versions. The entire process had taken four months, with only an eleven-day break.

PRIMARY SOURCE

In Their Words...

The Preamble, First Draft

We the People of the States of New-Hampshire, Massachusetts, Rhode-Island and Providence Plantations, Connecticut, New-York, New-Jersey, Pennsylvania, Delaware, Maryland, Virginia, North-Carolina, South-Carolina, and Georgia, do ordain, declare and establish the following Constitution for the Government of Ourselves and our Posterity.

—from the First Draft of the United States Constitution, August 6, 1787

Constitution [printing of first draft] [Committee of Detail], 6 August 1787, Philadelphia. Gilder Lehrman Collection #: GLC00819.01. Gilder Lehrman Institute of American History.

The Constitutional Convention delegates taking turns signing the Constitution

PRIMARY SOURCE

In Their Words...

The Preamble, Final Draft

We, the People of the United States, in order to form a more perfect union, establish justice, insure domestic tranquility, provide for the common defence, promote the general welfare, and secure the blessings of liberty to ourselves and our posterity, do ordain and establish this Constitution for the United States of America.

—from the official United States Constitution, September 17, 1787

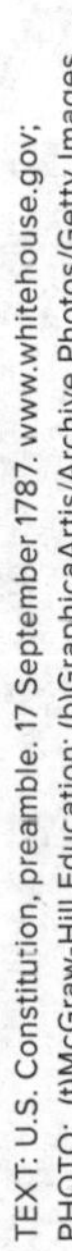

2 Find Evidence

Reread The Preamble lists five things the government must do: "establish justice, insure domestic tranquility, provide for the common defense, promote the general welfare, and secure the blessings of liberty to ourselves and our posterity, . . ."

Think of an example of how the government does each of these things. Compare your list of examples with lists from other students.

3 Make Connections

COLLABORATE

Write Imagine you are a delegate at the Constitutional Convention. Is there anything you think should be changed in the second version of the Preamble? Write a short speech explaining what you want added, changed, or removed, and why it is important.

Explore Making Inferences

To infer is to find a meaning that is not directly written or spoken. If a bill has trouble getting through Congress, you can infer that many people disagree with it. If a bill gets passed very quickly, on the other hand, then you can infer it was popular among members of Congress. These meanings that we find are called inferences.

When studying history, we often have to infer the reasons for historical persons' decisions, especially if they have not left behind diaries, letters, or other writing explaining their decisions. To make an inference:

1. **Read the text closely.**
   Make sure you understand what is being said.
2. **Recall what you know about the topic.**
   What do you know about the event being described? About the people involved? About what happened before and what came next?
3. **Combine what you know with what you have read.**
   Put the information together to form a more complete picture of what has happened.

What I Know	What I Read	My Inference
	The Preamble highlights several goals for drafting the U.S. Constitution.	

Investigate!

Read pages 266–277 in your Research Companion. Use your investigative skills to infer why some framers of the Constitution were concerned about either the Virginia Plan's or the New Jersey Plan's structure for a central government.

What I Know	What I Read	My Inference

Report Your Findings

Think About It

Look back on your research about the difficulties in writing the Constitution. How does the argument over the structure of the legislature illustrate the way the Constitution came to be written?

Write About It

Take a Stand

Write and Cite Evidence Write a dialogue between two delegates at the Constitutional Convention. The dialogue should show the opposing viewpoints in the dispute over the structure of the legislature, which eventually ended in the Great Compromise. In the dialogue, show each delegate's point of view and his reason for thinking that way.

Talk About It 

Act It Out

Work with a partner to read aloud or act out each other's dialogues. Afterwards, give your partner feedback. How did your partner illustrate the dispute and compromise?

Connect to the 

Pull It Together

What does the process of writing the Constitution reveal about our system of government?

Inquiry Project Notes

McGraw-Hill Education

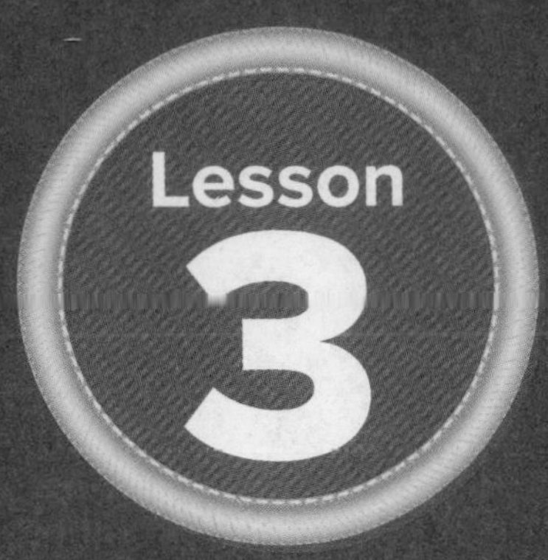

Lesson 3 How Do the Constitution and Bill of Rights Impact Citizens?

Lesson Outcomes

What Am I Learning?

In this lesson, you're going to use your investigative skills to explore how the Constitution and the Bill of Rights affect the people of the United States.

Why Am I Learning It?

Reading and talking about the liberties protected by the Constitution and the Bill of Rights will help you understand the rights of U.S. citizens.

How Will I Know That I Learned It?

You will be able to summarize how the lives of U.S. citizens are influenced by the country's founding documents.

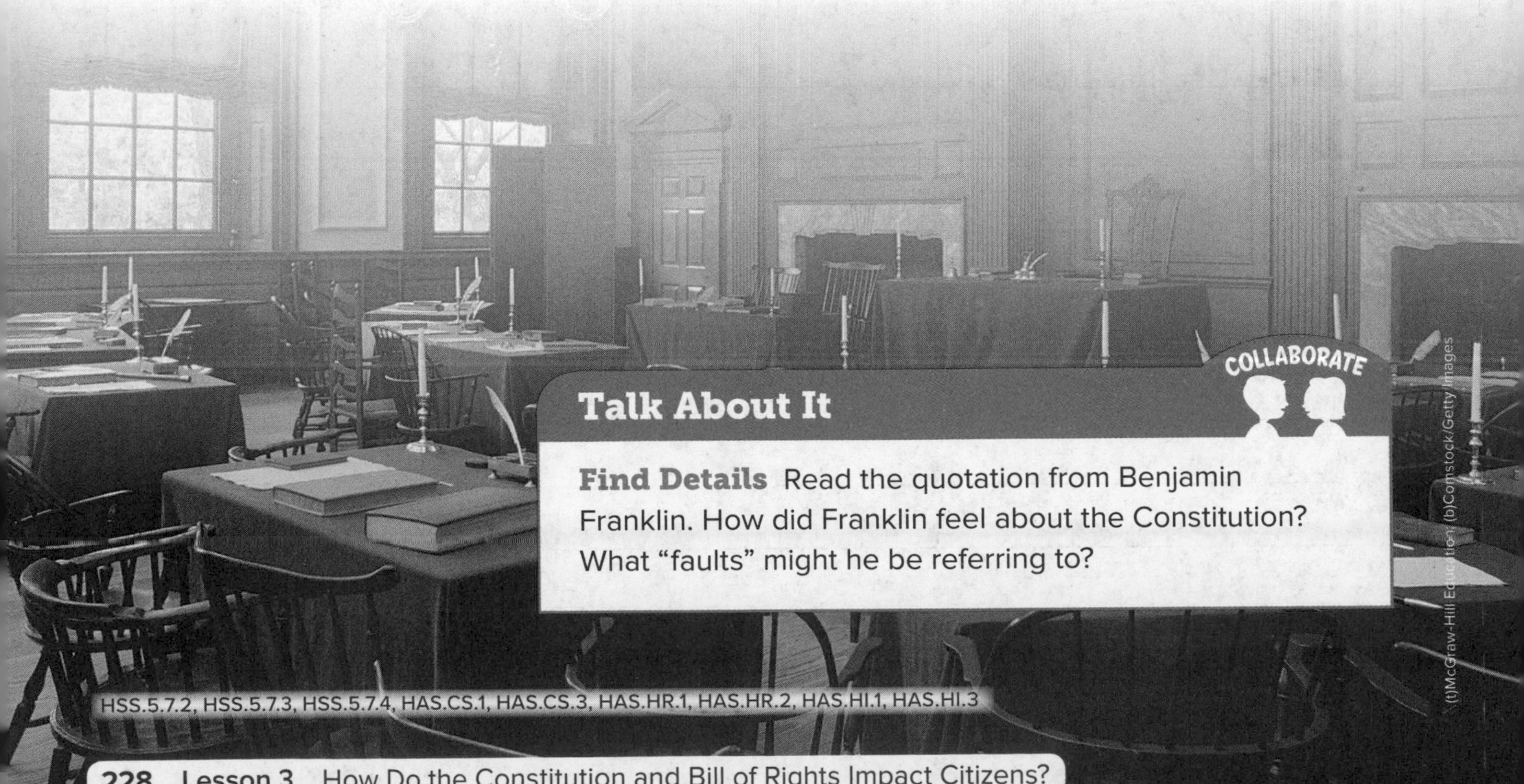

COLLABORATE

Talk About It

Find Details Read the quotation from Benjamin Franklin. How did Franklin feel about the Constitution? What "faults" might he be referring to?

HSS.5.7.2, HSS.5.7.3, HSS.5.7.4, HAS.CS.1, HAS.CS.3, HAS.HR.1, HAS.HR.2, HAS.HI.1, HAS.HI.3

PRIMARY SOURCE

In Their Words... Benjamin Franklin

I agree to this Constitution, with all its faults ... because I think a general Government necessary for us.... I doubt too, whether any other Convention we can obtain, may be able to make a better Constitution....

—Benjamin Franklin at the conclusion of the Constitutional Convention in 1787

Did You Know?

At the time of the Constitutional Convention, Ben Franklin was in his 80s and in poor health. Much of the convention occurred during summer months, and the hot room made Franklin even more uncomfortable. Yet, he played an important role at the convention, helping to calm things down when tempers flared. Franklin had many of his ideas shot down by other delegates. Among these was a belief that the executive branch should be led by a committee and that Congress should consist of only one house, not two. Nonetheless, Franklin supported the final version of the Constitution.

At the conclusion of the convention, Franklin noted to some of his fellow delegates that George Washington's chair had a half-sun on the back. For months, he had thought about the sun as a possible metaphor for the convention, and he told his colleagues he had wondered "whether it was rising or setting. But now at length I have the happiness to know that it is a rising and not a setting sun."

TEXT: Benjamin Franklin speaking to the Constitutional Convention, on September 17, 1787. From the notes of James Madison.; PHOTO: (t)McGraw-Hill Education; (r)kttimages/iStockphoto/Getty Images; (inset)Courtesy National Gallery of Art, Washington

The Freedoms of Religion and Expression

1 Inspect

Read Look at the titles "The Freedoms of Religion and Expression" and "The First Amendment." What connections are there between the two?

- **Circle** words you don't know.
- **Underline** words related to the concept of "The Freedoms of Religion and Expression."
- **Discuss** with a partner why the writers of the Bill of Rights chose the rights of expression and religious freedom to include as the first addition to the Constitution.

My Notes

____

____

____

____

____

____

____

____

____

The First Amendment of the Constitution protects Americans' freedoms of religion and expression. The amendment is intended to prevent the federal government from punishing citizens for what they say or what they believe. Since the writing of the Constitution, the Supreme Court has ruled on many cases concerning the First Amendment.

The Supreme Court has interpreted the First Amendment to grant four basic rights of expression. Freedom of speech gives people the right to share their ideas openly. Freedom of the press guarantees the right of the media to publish news freely. Freedom of assembly allows U.S. citizens to gather and hold meetings. Freedom of petition grants the right to sign petitions and to protest government policies. The broad freedoms of expression granted by the First Amendment made possible major U.S. protest campaigns such as the women's suffrage movement and the civil rights movement.

PRIMARY SOURCE

The First Amendment

Congress shall make no law respecting an establishment of religion, or prohibiting the free exercise thereof; or abridging the freedom of speech, or of the press; or the right of the people peaceably to assemble, and to petition the Government for a redress of grievances.

U.S. Constitution, amend. 1. (1791). www.senate.gov

The First Amendment gives U.S. citizens the right to express their opinions publicly.

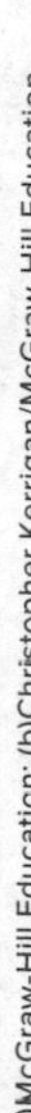

2 Find Evidence

Reread How does the author present the details of the First Amendment?

Examine Underline the transitional words and phrases that the author uses.

3 Make Connections

Draw Work with a partner to draw a chart of the five basic freedoms protected by the First Amendment. In one column, list the name of the freedom. In the next, list the right that it grants U.S. citizens. In the final column, list any exceptions that are not protected by the First Amendment.

COLLABORATE

Connect to Now How does the First Amendment affect the freedoms you enjoy today?

Summarize

When you write a summary, you list the most important details in a text. Your summary will help you remember and think about the structure of a text.

To write a summary:

1. **Read through the text.**
   This will help you determine the main idea of the text.
2. **Reread and jot down notes.**
   Make notes about the people, places, events, and ideas discussed. Make sure to include only details directly from the text, and not your opinions.
3. **List the most important details.**
   Write down the main details in the order that they appear in the text.
4. **Keep your summary brief.**
   Your summary should be shorter than the original text.

Based on the text you just read, work with your class to complete the chart below.

Details	The First Amendment to the Constitution protects Americans' freedoms of religion and expression.		
Summary			

Investigate!

Read pages 278–287 in your Research Companion. Use your investigative skills to list important details and to write a summary of one section of the text you read.

Details				
Summary				

Think About It

What is the purpose of the Bill of Rights?

Write About It

Give an Example

Illustrate Choose one right protected by the Bill of Rights. Write and illustrate a comic strip that shows that particular amendment in action.

Talk About It 

Explain

Work with a partner who chose a different amendment in the Bill of Rights. Read each other's comic strip, and discuss situations from your own lives in which the amendments would provide you with freedoms.

Citizenship

Connect to the 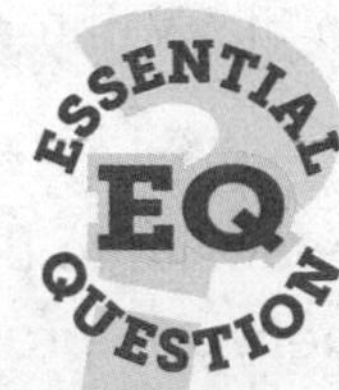

Pull It Together

How does the Bill of Rights help define what it means to be a citizen of the United States?

____

____

____

____

____

____

ESSENTIAL EQ QUESTION

Inquiry Project Notes

____

____

____

____

____

____

____

____

Project Wrap-Up

Now's the time for you and your classmates to present your conclusions. Here's what to do.

Use your notes and your class website to discuss your conclusions about the amendment you proposed.

- ☐ Work with your small group to write about your amendment and to respond to the other group's letters and editorials.
- ☐ Consider the opposing side's opinions. Think about how passing or not passing the amendment would impact the nation.
- ☐ Hold a class discussion in which your group presents your conclusions about the amendment. Make note of any opinions that the other group's writing helped to change.

Tips for Presenting

Remember these tips during your presentation.

- ☐ Be respectful of the points of view of your classmates.
- ☐ During your discussion, use evidence from the text and your class website or written correspondence about the amendment.
- ☐ Think about any points that you or your group should reconsider based on the other group's arguments.

Project Rubric

Use these questions to help evaluate your project.

	Yes	No
Did I research the topic related to the amendment?		
Did I participate in small-group discussions about our opinion on the amendment?		
Did I use information from the text and from our discussion to write a letter or an editorial about the amendment?		
Did I make my point of view clear?		
Did my group clearly present our side of the argument and our conclusions about the amendment?		

Project Reflection

Think about your work during this chapter. What was the most surprising or interesting thing you learned? What do you want to learn more about? What will you do differently in the future?

____

____

____

____

____

____

____

Life in the Young Republic

Lesson 1
Early Leaders and Decisions

Lesson 2
Advancements in Technology and Transportation

Lesson 3
People of the Young Republic

How Were the Early Years of the United States Transformative for the Nation?

In this chapter, you'll read about how the nation's first leaders made decisions that shaped the young United States. You'll also learn about the War of 1812 and conflicts with American Indians. In addition, you'll examine how important inventions made it easier to travel and communicate.

Talk About It

COLLABORATE

Discuss with a partner what questions you have about how the young United States grew and changed in its early years. As you research, look for answers to your questions. Let's get started!

My Research Questions

1. ______________________________

____

2. ______________________________

____

3. ______________________________

____

HSS.5.7.6, HSS.5.8.3; HAS.CS.3, HAS.HI.3

ESSENTIAL QUESTION EQ

Inquiry Project

Which Change Will You Choose?

In your opinion, which change during the early years of the United States had the biggest impact on the nation? Make a slideshow presentation on that change using images, video clips, songs, or other media. Explain what the change was, who was involved with the change, who was affected by the change, and what lasting impact the change has had on the nation. Use evidence from the text and outside sources.

Here's your project checklist.

- ☐ **Analyze** the task. Make sure you understand what you are expected to do.
- ☐ **Choose** an important change or innovation that you think had the greatest impact on the early years of the United States.
- ☐ **Conduct** research into that change, including the history of its development and information about any lasting effects it had on the nation. Take notes.
- ☐ **Use** your notes to create a presentation that makes a claim and supports it with evidence from the text and your research.
- ☐ **Conduct** research to find appropriate images, songs, videos, and other media.
- ☐ **Present** your information to the class.

Explore Words

Complete this chapter's Word Rater. Write notes as you learn more about each word.

cede

☐ Know It!
☐ Heard It!
☐ Don't Know It!

My Notes

composition

☐ Know It!
☐ Heard It!
☐ Don't Know It!

My Notes

corruption

☐ Know It!
☐ Heard It!
☐ Don't Know It!

My Notes

immigrant

☐ Know It!
☐ Heard It!
☐ Don't Know It!

My Notes

inland

☐ Know It!
☐ Heard It!
☐ Don't Know It!

My Notes

interchangeable

☐ Know It!
☐ Heard It!
☐ Don't Know It!

My Notes

loom

☐ Know It!
☐ Heard It!
☐ Don't Know It!

My Notes

policy

☐ Know It!
☐ Heard It!
☐ Don't Know It!

My Notes

reaping

☐ Know It!
☐ Heard It!
☐ Don't Know It!

My Notes

unconstitutional

☐ Know It!
☐ Heard It!
☐ Don't Know It!

My Notes

How Did Early Decisions Shape the Nation?

Lesson Outcomes

What Am I Learning?

In this lesson, you're going to use your investigative skills to learn about important events and government decisions in the early years of the United States.

Why Am I Learning It?

Reading and talking about those early events and decisions will help you understand the direction the nation took and what effects it had on the future.

How Will I Know That I Learned It?

You will be able to describe the causes and effects of important events in the nation's early years as well as the decisions and policies that the nation's early leaders made.

Talk About It

Look at the Details What object near the center of this image stands out among all the cannon fire? What is the artist suggesting with this image?

HSS.5.6.6, HSS.5.7.6, HSS.5.8.3, HAS.HR.1, HAS.HR.2, HAS.HI.1, HAS.HI.3

During the War of 1812, the British tried to capture Fort McHenry, just outside of Baltimore, Maryland.

Analyze the Source

1 Inspect

Read Look at the lyrics of this primary source and the sentences that introduce them.

- **Circle** words you don't know.
- **Underline** clues that tell you *what* event the text is about, *where* and *when* it takes place, and *how* and *why* it is happening.
- **Discuss** with a partner the event that Francis Scott Key witnessed.

My Notes

The Star-Spangled Banner

During the War of 1812, American Francis Scott Key was detained by the British on a ship in Baltimore Harbor. From the ship, he witnessed the British bombardment of Fort McHenry on September 13, 1814. The next morning, he saw the American flag still flying over the fort. He expressed his feelings in a poem that was later set to music. Known as "The Star-Spangled Banner," it eventually became the national anthem of the United States on March 3, 1931.

PRIMARY SOURCE

O say can you see, by the dawn's early light,

What so proudly we hail'd at the twilight's last gleaming,

Whose broad stripes and bright stars through the perilous fight

O'er the ramparts we watch'd were so gallantly streaming?

And the rocket's red glare, the bombs bursting in air,

Gave proof through the night that our flag was still there,

O say does that star-spangled banner yet wave

O'er the land of the free and the home of the brave?

– from "The Star-Spangled Banner" by Francis Scott Key

Key, Francis Scott. "The Star-Spangled Banner." Baltimore: Thomas Carr, 1814. American Treasures of the Library of Congress.

2 Find Evidence

Reread Look at the lyrics. What item or thing is the opening question about? Which details in the first two sentences make this clear? What is the significance of this item still being there "by the dawn's early light"?

3 Make Connections

Talk Discuss with a partner why the song is called "The Star-Spangled Banner."

Explore Cause and Effect

A **cause** is an event or action that is the reason something happens. An **effect** is the result of a cause. Often, a situation, event, or decision has more than one cause or more than one effect. Consider the causes and effects of government decisions and policies in the early years of the United States.

1. **Read the text once all the way through.**
   This will help you understand what the text is about.

2. **Look at the section titles to see how the text is organized.**
   This will help you find key events, decisions, and policies in the text.

3. **Find reasons or explanations.**
   While reading, ask yourself what specific reasons led to a particular decision or policy.

4. **Watch for specific changes.**
   While reading, also ask yourself what specific changes resulted from a particular decision or policy.

Based on the text you just read, work with your class to complete the chart below.

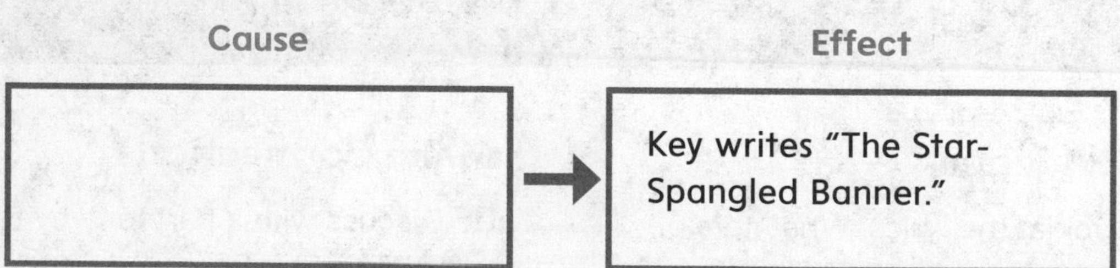

Investigate!

Read pages 298–309 in your Research Companion. Use your investigative skills to determine the effects of important decisions made in the early years of the United States. In the "Cause" column, write the decision. In the "Effect" column, describe how the decision impacted the nation.

Causes		Effects
	→	
	→	
	→	
	→	
	→	

Think About It

Review your research. Why was it important to explore the Louisiana Territory?

Write About It

Write a Diary Entry

Imagine you are someone living in the early United States who was affected by a decision or policy made by an early leader. Perhaps this person is an American Indian, a settler, or a member of the Corps of Discovery. Explain, in a diary entry from this person's perspective, how he or she was affected by the decision and why this decision was important. Remember to use evidence from the text.

Talk About It

COLLABORATE

Defend Your Claim

Working with a partner, discuss your diary entries. Take turns asking and answering questions that explain who each diary writer is, what that person has been doing, and how one or more government policies or decisions have affected him or her.

History

Connect to the ESSENTIAL EQ QUESTION

Consider Cause and Effect

Think about a policy or decision you wrote about in your diary entry. In general, how did it change the nation and its people?

ESSENTIAL EQ QUESTION

Inquiry Project Notes

Lesson 2 How Did Advancements in Technology and Transportation Shape the Nation?

Lesson Outcomes

What Am I Learning?

In this lesson, you will use your investigative skills to learn about new technology and transportation in the decades after the American Revolution and the way they affected the lives of U.S. citizens.

Why Am I Learning It?

Reading and talking about new technology and transportation will help you understand their importance in contributing to the growth of the U.S. economy and how they impacted people's lives.

How Will I Know That I Learned It?

You will be able to describe important inventions and other changes and how they addressed problems of travel and communication as well as how they affected the way people worked.

Talk About It

Look at the Details How are the different types of boats being powered? How can you tell?

HSS.5.8.1, HAS.HR.1, HAS.HR.2, HAS.HI.1, HAS.HI.2, HAS.HI.3

This painting of a river scene shows a flatboat used to transport goods and several passenger steamboats in the background.

Analyze the Source

1 Inspect

Read Examine the text of this primary source and the sentences that introduce it.

- **Circle** words you don't know.
- **Underline** details that tell you *what* the steamboat cabin is like, *where* Charles Dickens is going, and *when* he expects to arrive there.
- **Discuss** with a partner the opinions that Dickens seems to have about the steamboat.

My Notes

Charles Dickens Takes an American Steamboat

Britain's Charles Dickens was already a famous writer when he and his wife visited the United States in 1842. After stops on the East Coast, they traveled by canal boat, railroad, and stagecoach to Pittsburgh, Pennsylvania. From there, they took a steamboat called the *Messenger* down the Ohio River to Cincinnati, Ohio. Before the invention of the steamboat, travel by waterway took a long time and relied on the water's current. The following text comes from Dickens's description of that trip.

A caricature of the British author, Charles Dickens

PRIMARY SOURCE

In Their Words... Charles Dickens

The *Messenger* was one among a crowd of high-pressure steamboats, clustered together by a wharf side, which, looked down upon from the rising ground that forms the landing place, and backed by the lofty bank on the opposite side of the river, appeared no larger than so many floating models. She had some forty passengers on board, exclusive of the poorer persons on the lower deck; and in half an hour, or less, proceeded on her way.

We had, for ourselves, a tiny stateroom with two berths in it. . . . It was an unspeakable relief to have any place, no matter how confined, where one could be alone. . . .

We are to be on board the *Messenger* three days: arriving at Cincinnati (barring accidents) on Monday morning. There are three meals a day. Breakfast at seven, dinner at half-past twelve, supper about six. At each, there are a great many small dishes and plates upon the table, with very little in them; so that although there is every appearance of a mighty "spread," there is seldom really more than a joint: except for those who fancy slices of beet-root, shreds of dried beef, complicated entanglements of yellow pickle; maize, Indian corn, apple-sauce, and pumpkin.

—from *American Notes*, Chapter XI

2 Find Evidence

Reread What does the quotation show you about the two kinds of passengers on steamboats? Which kind of passenger is Charles Dickens?

3 Make Connections

Talk Discuss with a partner what you learn about steamboat travel from this primary source.

COLLABORATE

TEXT: Dickens, Charles. American Notes. New York: John W. Lovell Company, 1883.; PHOTO: McGraw-Hill Education

Explore Problem and Solution

Text is often organized by presenting problems and then showing how those problems have been or could be solved.

1. **Read the text once all the way through.**
   This will help you understand what the text is about.
2. **Look at the section titles to see how the text is organized.**
   This will help you find key events, decisions, and policies in the text.
3. **Find specific problems.**
   While reading, ask yourself what problems people in the early United States had.
4. **Watch for specific solutions.**
   While reading, also ask yourself which particular inventions or changes offered solutions to those problems.

Based on the text you just read, work with your class to complete the chart below.

Problem	Solution
Travel by waterway took a long time and was affected by the water's current.	

Investigate!

Read pages 310–317 in your Research Companion. Use your investigative skills to determine how advancements in technology and transportation solved various problems in the early United States. Use the chart below to organize the information.

Problem	Solution

Report Your Findings

Think About It

In the early 1800s, what was it like to communicate with someone living far away? Review your research to help you answer.

Write About It

Write an Advertisement

Develop an advertisement aimed at getting people to use one of the new technologies discussed in this lesson. Encourage those who are wary of the new technology to give it a try. Support your claims about the new technology with facts and details from the text. Sketch or describe a graphic to accompany your ad.

Talk About It

COLLABORATE

Compare Advertisements

Compare your advertisement with a partner's. Which is more likely to persuade people to use the new technology? Why?

History

Connect to the ESSENTIAL EQ QUESTION

Consider Cause and Effect

How did advances in transportation and communication shape the early United States?

ESSENTIAL EQ QUESTION

Inquiry Project Notes

McGraw-Hill Education

Who Were the People Living in the Early United States?

Lesson Outcomes

What Am I Learning?

In this lesson, you're going to use your investigative skills to explore the various people who lived in the early United States, including the first pioneers, American Indians, African Americans, and immigrants.

Why Am I Learning It?

Reading and talking about the lives of the people who lived in the early United States will help you understand how people's experiences in the young nation were affected by their race, ethnicity, and gender.

How Will I Know That I Learned It?

You will be able to compare and contrast the experiences of three groups of people who lived in the early United States in a short blog post. Then you will support your findings with facts and details from the text.

Talk About It

Find Details Read the words to "America the Beautiful." What kind of country does the author describe?

HSS.5.3.4, HSS.5.3.6, HSS.5.4.6, HSS.5.8.1, HSS.5.8.4, HAS.HI.2

O beautiful for spacious skies,

For amber waves of grain,

For purple mountains majesties

Above the fruited plain!

America! America! God shed his grace on thee,

And crown thy good with brotherhood

From sea to shining sea!

—from "America, the Beautiful"
By Katherine Lee Bates — 1913

"Amber Waves of Grain": A Wheat Field

TEXT: Bates, Katherine Lee. "America the Beautiful." 1893.;
PHOTO: (bkgd)Design Pics/Darren Greenwood; (inset)Kittimages/iStockphoto/Getty Images

1 Inspect

Read Look at the title. What do the words "letter to her mother" suggest about the kind of text this will be?

- **Circle** words you don't know.
- **Underline** clues that help you answer the questions *who, what, where, when,* or *why.*
- **Discuss** with a partner how Cathy Greene feels and what her experience as a recent immigrant has been like.

My Notes

Cathy Greene Writes a Letter to Her Mother

Irish immigrants escaping poverty and famine in their own country faced many difficulties once they arrived in the United States. New York City, for example, was very different from the Irish countryside. The environment for many was strange and frightening. In addition, within a very short time, immigrants had to make sure that practical needs were met. They needed to find a place to stay. They needed to find a job in order to support themselves. And then, many experienced the crushing weight of loneliness. They had to leave home; there was very little opportunity there. But they missed home and their families, often intensely.

Cathy Greene, a recent Irish immigrant living in Brooklyn, New York, wrote to her mother in County Kilkenny, Ireland, in 1884, begging her to write her back.

In the mid-1800s, many Irish immigrants came to the United States hoping to escape poverty and starvation.

Avella/Shutterstock.com

PRIMARY SOURCE

In Their Words... Cathy Greene

My Dear Mama,

What on earth is the matter with ye all, that none of you would think of writing to me? The fact is I am heart-sick, fretting. I cannot sleep the night and if I chance to sleep I wake with the most frightful dreams.

To think that it's now going and gone into the third month since ye wrote to me. I feel as if I'm dead to the world. I've left the place I was employed. They failed in business. I was out of place all summer and the devil knows how long. This is a world of troubles. I would battle with the world and would never feel dissatisfied if I would hear often for ye ... I know if I don't hear from ye prior to the arrival of this letter...I will be almost dead."

—from Cathy Greene's letter to her mother, August 1, 1884

2 Find Evidence

Reread Notice the problems Cathy Greene has to deal with. How do you think these problems affect her anxiety over not hearing from her mother?

Reread the line "I would battle with the world and never feel dissatisfied if I would hear often from ye." What is Cathy Greene trying to tell her mother in these lines?

3 Make Connections

Talk Discuss with a partner the many feelings an immigrant might feel when family members are far away.

COLLABORATE

TEXT: Cathy Greene, Brooklyn, NY, to her mother, Ballylarkin, Callan, County Kilkenny, 1 August 1884. Greene/Norris Family Papers, Archives Department, University College, Dublin.; PHOTO: McGraw-Hill Education

Explore Compare and Contrast

Comparing and contrasting groups of people in the early United States will help you understand how the experiences of the groups are alike and different.

1. **Read the text all the way through.**
   This will help you understand what the text is about.
2. **Look for groups of people whose experiences are described.**
   This will help you help you decide which groups of people you will compare and contrast.
3. **Choose three groups that you can easily compare and contrast.**
   This will help you analyze the experience of three groups of people.
4. **List the main experiences of each group and how they are similar to or different from the experience of other groups.**
   This will help you find likenesses and differences among the groups.

COLLABORATE Based on the text you just read, work with your class to describe the experiences of immigrants and to compare them to the experiences of another group you know of.

Group	Experiences	Likenesses/Differences
Immigrants		

Investigate!

Read pages 318–327 in your Research Companion. Use your investigative skills to identify different groups of people and their experiences. Then compare their experiences with those of a different group.

Group	Experiences	Likenesses/Differences

Report Your Findings

Think About It

How were people's experiences in the early United States different depending on their race, ethnicity, or gender?

Write About It

Write a Blog Post

Choose three groups of people who lived in the young United States. Compare and contrast their experiences in a short blog post. Use facts and details from the text in your comparison-contrast blog.

Talk About It

Share Your Thinking

Exchange your blog post with that of a partner. What likenesses or similarities did your partner include that you did not?

Connect to the

Pull It Together

What were the early years of the United States like for different groups of people?

____

____

____

____

____

____

ESSENTIAL EQ QUESTION

Inquiry Project Notes

____

____

____

____

____

____

____

____

Project Wrap-Up

Now's the time for you and your classmates to give your presentations.

Use your presentation to support your opinion about which change had the biggest impact on the young United States.

- ☐ Reread your presentation to make sure it clearly states your opinion and supporting evidence.
- ☐ Review the media you chose. Each visual element should add something important to the presentation, not distract from it.
- ☐ Take questions from your audience after presenting. Support your responses with evidence from the text and from your research.

Tips for Presenting

Remember these tips during your presentation.

- ☐ Speak slowly and clearly.
- ☐ While reading your notes, look up often to make eye contact with audience members.
- ☐ Remember to point to your slideshow to reinforce what you are telling your audience.
- ☐ Carefully consider any questions. If you don't know an answer, explain that you'll do more research and report back.

Project Rubric

Use these questions to help evaluate your project.

	Yes	No
Did I choose an important change that affected the early United States?		
Did I conduct enough research to clearly explain the change and support my opinion about it?		
Did I create a presentation that is easy to follow and understand?		
Did I choose images, video, and other media that add to my presentation rather than distract from it?		
Did I present my slideshow clearly, using my notes and referring to the visuals often?		

Project Reflection

Think about your work during this chapter. What work did you like best? What topic do you want to learn more about? What will you do differently with your work on future chapters?

____

____

____

____

____

____

____

The Westward Expansion

Lesson 1
Stories of the Settlers

Lesson 2
Hard Times for American Indians

Lesson 3
California and Texas Join the Union

What Does the Westward Expansion Reveal About the Character of Our Nation?

In this chapter, you'll read about how the United States expanded westward. You'll understand the obstacles that settlers faced along the journey west, and you'll examine the hardships of American Indians as a result of U.S. expansion.

COLLABORATE

Talk About It

Discuss with a partner what questions you have about how the United States expanded westward. As you research, look for answers to your questions. Let's get started!

My Research Questions

1. ______________________________

____

2. ______________________________

____

3. ______________________________

____

HSS.5.3.6, HSS.5.8.4, HSS.5.8.6, HAS.HR.2

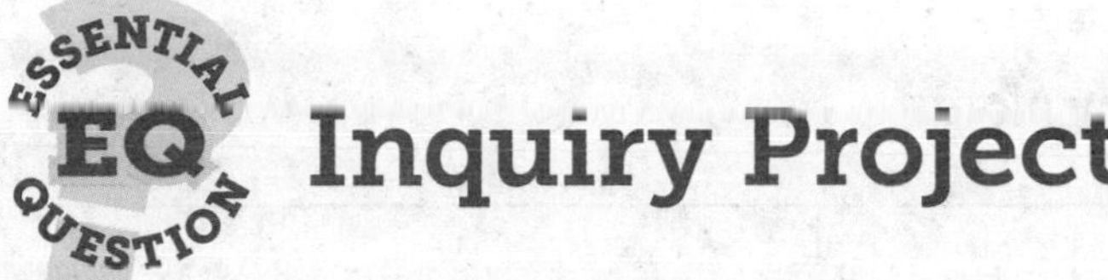

Inquiry Project

Create a Museum Gallery

Create a gallery (print or digital) of three paintings that depict westward expansion. Write a museum card for each picture by including the title, the name of the artist, the year it was painted, and a brief description of what the painting shows. Discuss as a group how the paintings work together to tell a story of how the United States grew and expanded west.

Here's your project checklist.

- ☐ **Analyze** the task. Make sure you understand what you are expected to do.
- ☐ **Conduct** research to find three paintings that depict U.S. westward expansion.
- ☐ **Find** information about each painting. Determine what you like and dislike about each painting. Take notes.
- ☐ **Create** a museum card for each painting with the facts and details from your research.
- ☐ **Present** each image and its card to the class. Explain why you chose each painting as you tell about its history.

Explore Words

Complete this chapter's Word Rater. Write notes as you learn more about each word.

boundary

☐ Know It!
☐ Heard It!
☐ Don't Know It!

My Notes

hostility

☐ Know It!
☐ Heard It!
☐ Don't Know It!

My Notes

Manifest Destiny

☐ Know It!
☐ Heard It!
☐ Don't Know It!

My Notes

oxen

☐ Know It!
☐ Heard It!
☐ Don't Know It!

My Notes

republic

☐ Know It!
☐ Heard It!
☐ Don't Know It!

My Notes

sovereign

☐ Know It!
☐ Heard It!
☐ Don't Know It!

My Notes

____
____
____

surge

☐ Know It!
☐ Heard It!
☐ Don't Know It!

My Notes

____
____
____

survey

☐ Know It!
☐ Heard It!
☐ Don't Know It!

My Notes

____
____
____

territory

☐ Know It!
☐ Heard It!
☐ Don't Know It!

My Notes

____
____
____

veto

☐ Know It!
☐ Heard It!
☐ Don't Know It!

My Notes

____
____
____

What Did Settlers Experience in Their Movement Westward?

Lesson Outcomes

What Am I Learning?

In this lesson, you're going to use your investigative skills to learn about what U.S. settlers experienced as they moved farther west.

Why Am I Learning It?

Reading and talking about what the settlers experienced will help you understand why the move west was important.

How Will I Know That I Learned It?

You will be able to ask and answer questions about the settlers' experiences as they moved west, and you will write a travel guide.

Talk About It

Look at the Details What would it have been like to live in a wagon and travel a trail westward for six months?

HSS.5.8.2, HSS.5.8.4, HSS.5.8.6, HAS.CS.4

A covered wagon at Scotts Bluff National Monument

David Sucsy/iStock/Getty Images

1 Inspect

View Look at the image. What is the picture showing?

- **Think** about the figures shown in the painting.
- **Examine** clues that help you understand what event each part of the picture shows.
- **Discuss** why you think the artist painted it.

My Notes

What Is Manifest Destiny?

In the 1800s, people who struggled on the East Coast found the prospect of settling the open territory of the West appealing. They wanted to make the trip despite the obstacles they would face on the long, slow journey. This drive to settle the West was known as Manifest Destiny. It eventually led to the United States stretching from the Atlantic to the Pacific.

Many works of art explore the openness and natural beauty of the West. John Gast's painting *American Progress* shows major advances such as the telegraph, the stagecoach, and the steam engine. This progress is represented by the figure of a woman moving gracefully from the East to the West. The book she is carrying shows that she is bringing along civilization's knowledge.

Opponents of Manifest Destiny pointed out that it ignored the rights of native peoples living in the West and disrespected their ways of life. Many settlers believed that it was God's will for the nation to expand westward. These settlers believed that their way of life and their religion ought to dominate the continent from East to West.

John Gast was a Prussian-born artist who lived in Brooklyn. He was known for allegorical, or symbolic, painting. George Crofutt, the publisher of the era's most popular travel guides, commissioned the painting *American Progress* in 1872 from Gast. This was more than twenty years after the concept of Manifest Destiny was born. Crofutt published the reproductions of the painting in his Western travel guides, where thousands saw the image.

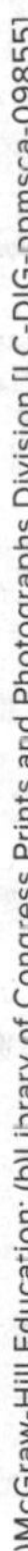

American Progress by John Gast

2 Find Evidence

Look Again Examine the woman at the center of the picture. What is she holding? From which direction does she seem to be coming? Where is she going? Is this a portrait of a real woman? What might she represent?

Examine Read the statement "John Gast's painting *American Progress* shows major advances such as the telegraph, the stagecoach, and the steam engine." Why do you think Gast included these in the painting?

3 Make Connections

Talk Do you think those who saw this painting reprinted in travel guides at the time of westward expansion would have been inspired to travel west? Do you think American Indians would have been offended by this painting? Why or why not?

Inquiry Tools

Explore Asking and Answering Questions

You can better understand what you read if you ask and answer questions about it. Support your answers with evidence from the text.

1. **Read the text all the way through.**
   This will help you understand what the text is about.
2. **Reread the text, looking for key details.**
   Locate the important information, facts, or evidence in the text.
3. **Ask yourself about the important people and events in the text.**
   This will help you identify ideas or information you may have missed.
4. **Answer your questions using evidence from the text.**
   This will help you clarify your understanding of what you've read.

Based on the source you just studied, work with your class to complete the chart below.

Question	Answer	Text Evidence
Why was Gast's painting titled *American Progress*?		

Investigate!

Read pages 340–345 in your Research Companion. Use your investigative skills to look for text evidence that tells you about important events and people.

Question	Answer	Text Evidence

Report Your Findings

Think About It

Review your research. What was it like to move west in the early 1800s?

Write About It

Write a Travel Guide

Choose a trail and write a short travel guide for people living in the East who were considering moving west. Make your travel guide convincing by including details about landmarks, the comforts and companionship of trail life, and the opportunities available on arrival in the Oregon Territory.

Talk About It

Defend Your Claims

Work with a partner who chose a different trail. Which travel guide would you be more likely to believe? What are some of the hardships that both travel guides do not mention?

Connect to the

Make Connections

What drove people to settle in the West despite challenges and dangers?

____

____

____

____

____

____

ESSENTIAL EQ QUESTION

Inquiry Project Notes

____

____

____

____

____

____

____

____

How Did Westward Expansion Impact American Indians?

Lesson Outcomes

What Am I Learning?

In this lesson, you're going to use your investigative skills to explore events that impacted the lives of American Indians in the 1800s.

Why Am I Learning It?

Reading and talking about these events will help you understand their impact on American Indians and the current state of American Indians and the nation.

How Will I Know That I Learned It?

You will be able to identify Andrew Jackson's point of view about the Indian Removal Act and make an argument against the act.

Talk About It

Look at the Details What does the painting show? What does the title of the painting suggest about the event?

HSS.5.3.4, HSS.5.3.5, HSS.5.3.6, HAS.CS.5, HAS.HR.1, HAS.HR.2, HAS.HI.1

SuperStock

The Trail of Tears by Robert Lindneux

Analyze the Source

1 Inspect

Read Look at the first line of the quotation on the next page. Which words provoke strong emotions in you?

- **Circle** unfamiliar words.
- **Underline** clues that show that American Indians were forced to leave.
- **Discuss** with a partner how John G. Burnett feels about the event. What words does he use to describe what he saw?

My Notes

Witnessing the Trail of Tears

In the 1800s, the nation began expanding westward rapidly. By 1824, about 3 million people, or 30 percent of the U.S. population, lived on the frontier.

Treaties between American Indians and the U.S. government guaranteed native people's rights to their land in these regions. Initially, settlers respected the treaties and lived peacefully alongside American Indians. Settlers soon demanded more land, however, triggering conflict. President Andrew Jackson supported the seizure of American Indians' lands and used the office of the presidency to break the treaties.

In 1830, Congress passed the Indian Removal Act. This forced American Indians in the southeastern United States to leave their homes and march about 800 miles into present-day Oklahoma. Despite a Supreme Court ruling against the act, President Jackson defied the highest court in the land and ordered soldiers to round up Cherokee and burn their homes. Of the 15,000 Cherokee forced to relocate 800 miles west, 4,000 died.

John G. Burnett, a young U.S. soldier who spoke Cherokee, served as an interpreter on the Trail of Tears. The Cherokee called him "the soldier who was good to us." In an 1890 publication, Burnett reflected on what he saw during the 800-mile "Trail of Tears."

PRIMARY SOURCE

In Their Words... John G. Burnett

[In] May 1838 ... I saw helpless Cherokee arrested and dragged from their homes . ... I saw them loaded like cattle or sheep into six hundred and forty-five wagons and starting toward the west. . . . Many of the children rose to their feet and waved their little hands good-by to their mountain homes, knowing they were leaving them forever. Many of . . . them had been driven from home barefooted.

On the morning of November the 17th we encountered a terrific sleet and snow storm with freezing temperatures and from that day until we reached the end of the fateful journey on March the 26th, 1839, the sufferings of the Cherokees were awful. The trail of the exiles was a trail of death. They had to sleep in the wagons and on the ground without fire. And I have known as many as twenty-two of them to die in one night of pneumonia due to ill treatment, cold, and exposure. . . .

The long painful journey to the west ended March 26th, 1839, with four-thousand silent graves reaching from the foothills of the Smoky Mountains to what is known as Indian territory in the West...

Somebody must explain the streams of blood that flowed in the Indian country in the summer of 1838. Somebody must explain the 4000 silent graves that mark the trail of the Cherokees to their exile. I wish I could forget it all, but the picture of 645 wagons lumbering over the frozen ground with their Cargo of suffering humanity still lingers in my memory.

—from *Story of the Trail of Tears*, published in 1890

2 Find Evidence

Reread Notice how John Burnett gives vivid details to help readers picture what he saw and heard on the journey.

Examine Read the statement "Somebody must explain the 4000 silent graves that mark the trail of the Cherokees to their exile." What impact does this image of "silent graves" have on the reader emotionally? What do you think Burnett hoped to achieve by writing this?

3 Make Connections

Talk Discuss with a partner the details in Burnett's story that show the hardships of the Trail of Tears. How does Burnett's description reveal his own viewpoint about the event?

COLLABORATE

TEXT: Burnett, John G. 1838-39. Removal of the Cherokee 1838-1839. The King Research Collection: Trail of Tears. Museum of the Cherokee Indian [2009.003.0577].; PHOTO: McGraw-Hill Education

Inquiry Tools

Explore Point of View

A person's point of view is his or her opinion on a topic. Determining point of view can help you understand a person's choices and actions.

1. **Identify opinion words.**
   Which words indicate that someone's opinion is being conveyed? Which words express positive or negative emotions?
2. **Look for reasons and evidence.**
   What reasoning and supporting details can you find that support his or her point of view?
3. **Identify actions and choices.**
   What important decisions or actions does the person make?
4. **Evaluate actions for point of view.**
   Ask yourself, Did this person's point of view impact his or her actions?

Based on the text you just read, work with your class to fill in the details that support the point of view in the center oval.

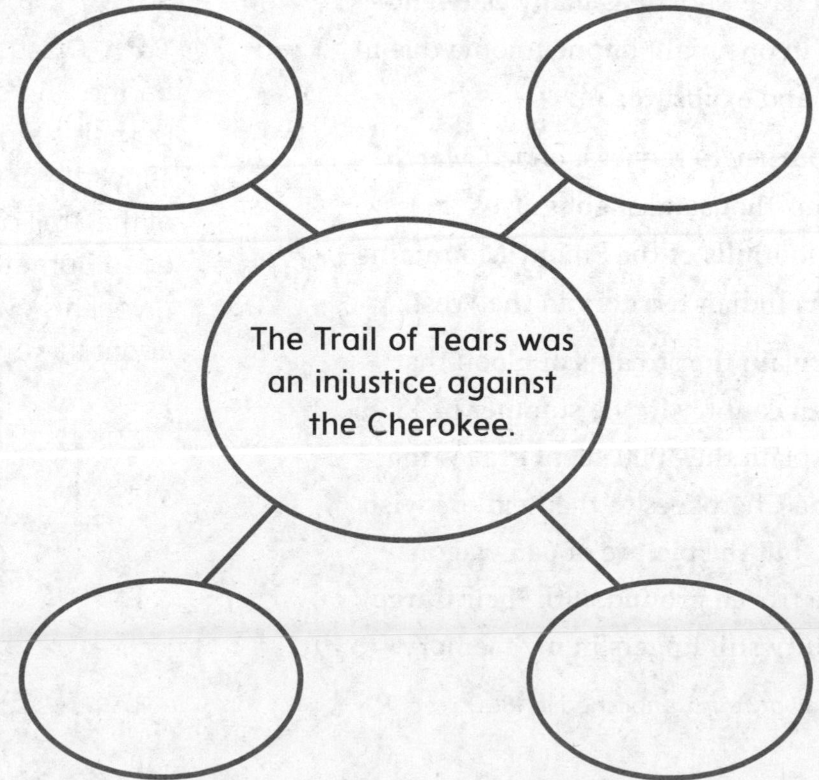

Investigate!

Read pages 346–353 in your Research Companion. Use your investigative skills to determine President Andrew Jackson's point of view about the removal of American Indians from their lands. Use the organizer to track key details that support this point of view.

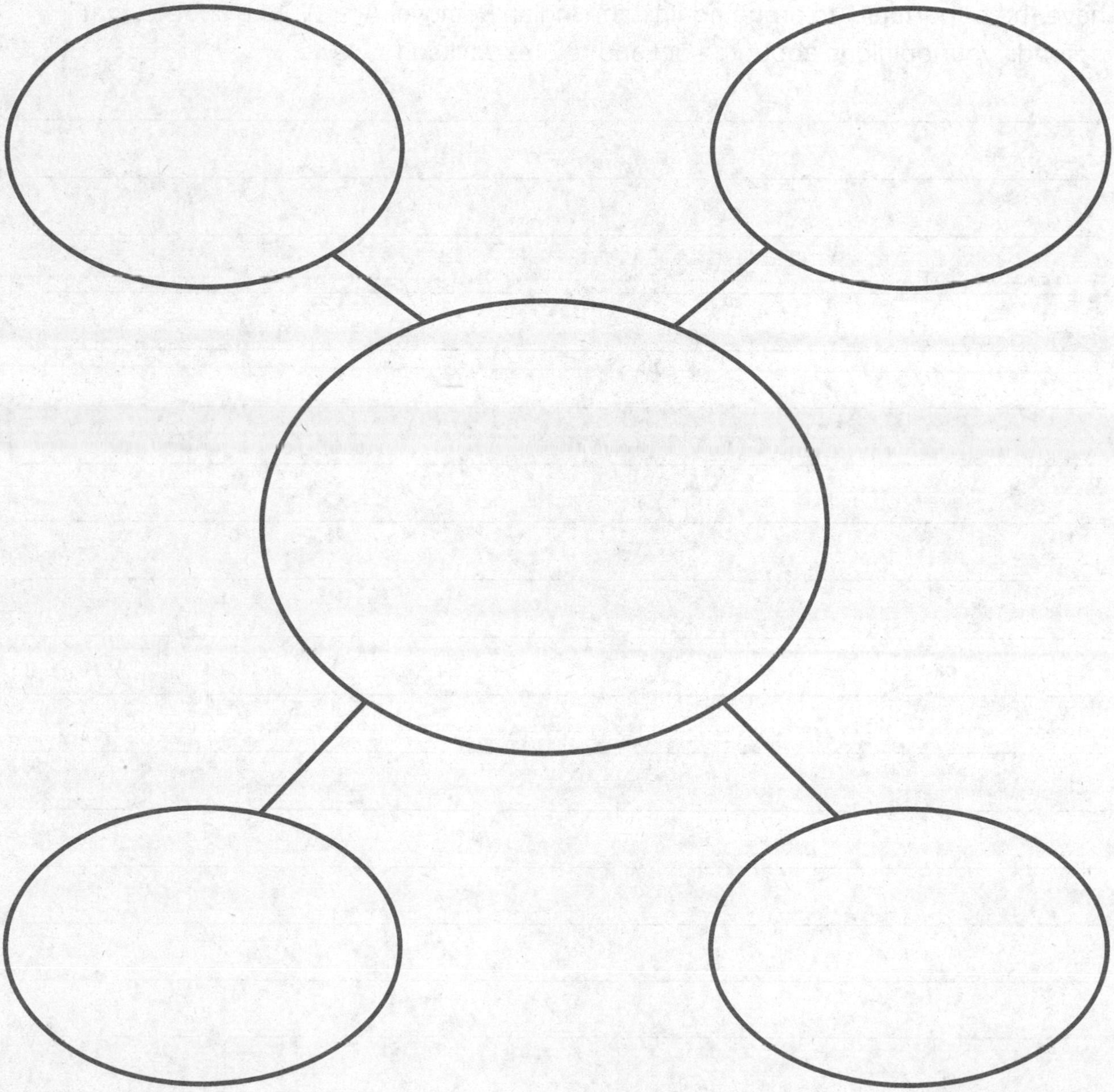

Report Your Findings

Think About It

What was the effect of Andrew Jackson's opinions about American Indian removal?

Write About It

Take a Stand

Write and Cite Evidence Imagine you are a senator in Congress in 1830, and you have the opportunity to argue against the Indian Removal Act. Write a speech that defends your opinions about the act and refutes Jackson's views.

Talk About It

Defend Your Claim

Work with a partner, and compare your speeches. Which of your speeches is the most convincing, and why?

Connect to the

Pull It Together

How is the Indian Removal Act in conflict with the spirit in which the United States was founded? What does the Indian Removal Act reveal about the character of the nation at that time?

____

____

____

____

____

____

____

____

____

Inquiry Project Notes

____

____

____

____

____

How Did California and Texas Become Part of the United States?

Lesson Outcomes

What Am I Learning?

In this lesson, you're going to use your investigative skills to explore the events that led to statehood for Texas and California.

Why Am I Learning It?

Reading and talking about these events will help you understand their impact on Texas, California, and the nation.

How Will I Know That I Learned It?

You will be able to identify the causes and effects of the Mexican-American War, explain how that event affected the United States, and support that explanation with evidence.

Talk About It

Look at the Details What is Davy Crockett doing? What does this depiction tell you about how settlers viewed the Texans who fought at the Alamo?

HSS.5.8.4, HSS.5.8.5, HSS.5.8.6, HAS.HI.3

Pioneer and folk hero Davy Crockett fought in the Battle of the Alamo, won by Mexico.

Ed Vebell/Archive Photos/Getty Images

Analyze the Source

Sam Houston's Letter to Andrew Jackson

1 Inspect

Read Scan the excerpt from Sam Houston's letter. What is Houston's main idea?

- **Circle** repeated phrases.
- **Underline** words that change within those phrases.
- **Discuss** with a partner how Houston's phrasing makes his ideas sound more convincing or powerful.

My Notes

General Sam Houston won the Battle of San Jacinto, and Houston was praised as a hero. His victory after the loss at the Alamo helped form Texas's identity as a unified state. With Texas's independence from Mexico secured, he was elected as president of the brand-new Republic of Texas.

Houston held the office from 1836 to 1838 and again from 1841 to 1844. During his second term, Houston also played a key role in finally securing statehood for Texas in 1845. He wrote to many U.S. leaders, including former President Andrew Jackson, arguing that Texas should be annexed, or added, to the United States. Once Texas became a state, he became one of the state's first United States senators.

Sam Houston

PRIMARY SOURCE

In Their Words... Sam Houston

So far as I am concerned, or my hearty cooperation required, I am determined upon immediate annexation to the United States.

It is not the result of feeling, nor can I believe that the measure would be as advantageous to Texas, as it is indispensably necessary to the United States. Texas, with peace, could exist without the United States, but the United States cannot without great hazard to the security of their institutions exist without Texas. The United States are one of the rival powers of earth, and from their importance, as well as the peculiarity of their institutions and the extent of their commercial relations, they must expect, at no distant day, wars, the object of which will be to prevent their continuance, if possible, as a nation.

—from a letter to Andrew Jackson, February 16, 1844

TEXT: Sam Houston to Andrew Jackson, Washington, TX, 16 February 1844. In Life and Select Literary Remains of Sam Houston of Texas, by William Carey Crane. Philadelphia: J.B. Lippincott Company, 1884.;
PHOTO: McGraw-Hill Education

2 Find Evidence

Reread Identify what Houston wants to do. Why does he feel so strongly about his goal?

Reread the claim Houston makes in this letter. What events in history support the idea that Texas can exist without the United States?

3 Make Connections

Talk Discuss with a partner why Sam Houston felt so strongly about Texas. How might adding Texas to the Union strengthen the United States?

COLLABORATE

Connect to Now How does the inclusion of Texas in the United States make the United States stronger today?

Explore Cause and Effect

As you read, identifying the relationship between historical events will help you understand how and why the events happened.

1. **Read the text once all the way through.**
   This will help you understand the main ideas.

2. **Identify key events.**
   As you read, think about which events seem to be related.

3. **Look for signal words and phrases.**
   Words and phrases such as *because, consequently, thus,* and *as a result* show a cause-and-effect relationship.

4. **Examine cause and effect.**
   Remember that a **cause** is an event or action that makes something happen. An **effect** is what happens as a result of that cause. Many events in history happen as a direct result of other events.

Based on the text you have just read, work with your class to complete the chart below.

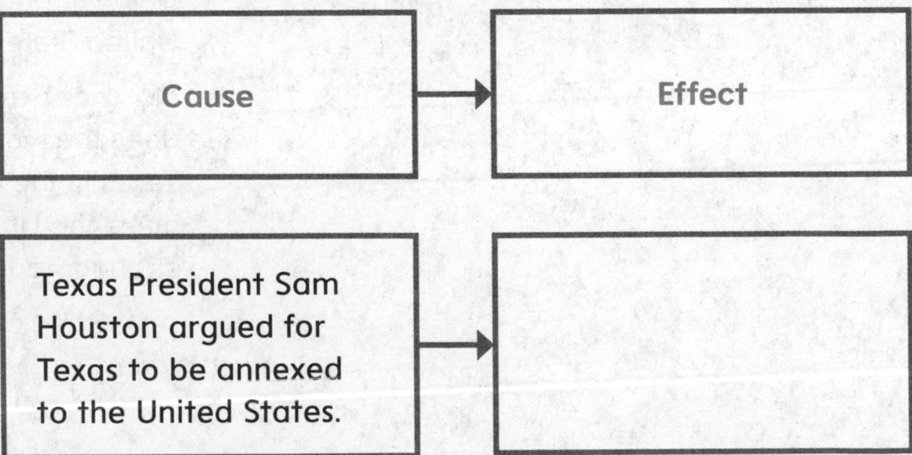

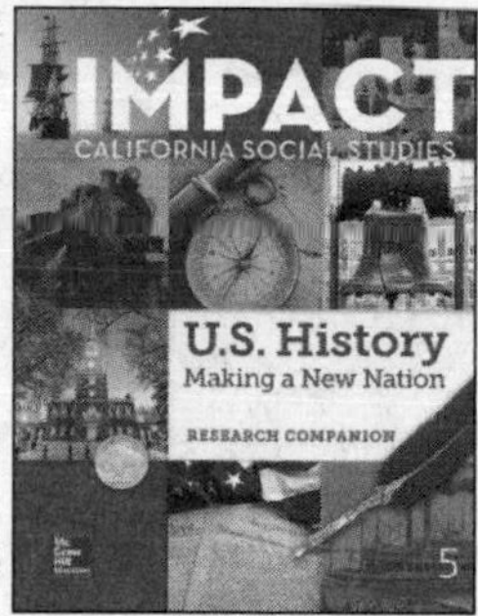

Investigate!

Read pages 354–363 in your Research Companion. Use your investigative skills to identify key events that led to statehood for Texas and California. Use the chart to organize information.

Cause	→	Effect
	→	
	→	
	→	

McGraw-Hill Education

Report Your Findings

Think About It

Take a Stand

Review your research. Based on the information you have gathered, what do you think was so important about the southwest territories that caused disputes between Mexico and the United States?

Write About It

Write an Article

Write an article about the outcome of the Mexican-American War. Identify what the United States gained and how it changed the country. Cite evidence from the text.

Talk About It

Defend Your Claim

Work with a partner. Discuss how the Treaty of Guadalupe Hidalgo changed the makeup of the United States.

History

Connect to the

Pull It Together

What did the outcome of the war with Mexico reveal about the spirit and character of the young United States?

ESSENTIAL EQ QUESTION

Inquiry Project Notes

Project Wrap-Up

Now's the time for you and your classmates to present your paintings and museum cards.

Use your notes to present your paintings.

- ☐ Project or pass out copies of your paintings so your audience can look closely at the details in each one.
- ☐ Read aloud the museum card you wrote for each painting. Explain what you like and dislike about each painting.
- ☐ Take questions from your audience after presenting. Support your responses with evidence from your research.

Tips for Presenting

Remember these tips during your presentation.

- ☐ Speak slowly and clearly.
- ☐ Refer often to the paintings, and discuss details that audience members can see and analyze for themselves.
- ☐ To make your analysis clearer, zoom in on specific details as you discuss the paintings, if possible.

Project Rubric

Use these questions to help evaluate your project.

	Yes	No
Did I choose three paintings that depict westward expansion?		
Did I conduct research about each painting to find out its title, its artist, its year of creation, and information about what it shows?		
Did I create a museum card for each painting that included important facts and details?		
Did I present each painting in a way that was clear and easy to follow?		
Did I refer to the details in each painting so my audience could understand my analysis?		

Project Reflection

Think about your work during this chapter. What did you enjoy most? Which painting did you like best? What will you do differently next time you conduct research?

____

____

____

____

____

____

The California Gold Rush

CHARACTERS

Narrator

Susanna Jones *(owner of a general store)*

Louisa Lansdown *(sister of Joe)*

Malcolm Roberts *(husband of Lily)*

Joe Lansdown *(brother of Louisa)*

Martin Baker

Lily Roberts *(wife of Malcolm)*

Narrator: In December 1848, President James K. Polk announced that gold had been found in the California hills. Soon thousands of people traveled west to mine for gold. They dreamed of striking it rich. These men and women became known as the Forty-niners because they made their journey in 1849.

Louisa and Joe Lansdown are Forty-niners. They have just arrived in California. The young brother and sister head to a general store for supplies.

(Susanna *arranges goods on the store counter.* Louisa *and* Joe *burst through the door.)*

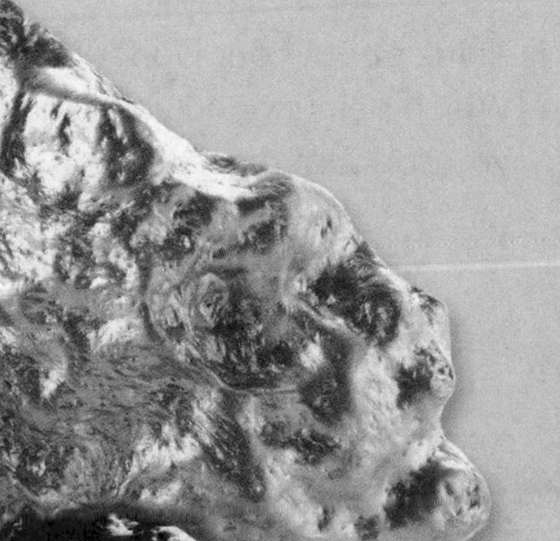

sumire8/Shutterstock.com

Joe: Excuse me, ma'am; my sister and I would like to buy some supplies.

Susanna: Where are you folks from?

Joe: Maryland. We came by wagon. It took months!

Louisa: We're going to get rich. I can't wait to start digging for gold!

Susanna: I'll show you a few things that every miner needs.

(Martin *enters with a hand pressed to his back.)*

Martin: Oh my aching back!

Susanna: Don't pay any attention to him. He's always complaining!

Martin: Before I left home, I figured it would be a year of pain for a lifetime of riches. Well, I guess I got the pain part!

Joe: And you got rich too, right?

Martin: HA! All I got was backbreaking labor. Ten hours a day, knee-deep in ice-cold water: digging, sifting, washing. Panning dirt just to find more dirt! Never so much as a twinkling lump of rock, much less gold.

Susanna: People are coming from all around the world to strike it rich. I've seen folks from Mexico, Ireland, Germany, France—even Turkey!

Martin: Every day there are more miners and less and less gold.

Susanna: (Susanna *is starting to worry about making a sale. She tries to be positive.)* So you'll need good tools! I have a shovel that will dig through just about anything. Take a look.

Louisa: Wait a minute. Are you saying that you didn't find *any* gold, sir?

Martin: Young lady, do I look like a wealthy man? Ow!

Susanna: Now back to those supplies. I can give you a great deal on this pan — only twenty dollars!

Joe: Twenty dollars! That's half our savings!

Susanna: Blame it on Sam Billington, the wealthiest man in California!

Just before the Gold Rush, he bought every pickax, pan, and shovel for miles around. By the time Forty-niners like you arrived, Sam Billington was sitting on his own gold mine. Can't mine without tools, right?

Martin: There's always someone looking to separate a hardworking man from his money.

(Malcolm *enters, holding an empty bottle, limping a little bit.)*

Malcolm: Susanna! You have any more of that lotion?

Susanna: Sure. I'll be right back.

(She leaves the room to look in the storage closet.)

Louisa: What kind of lotion is it?

Malcolm: It's a gold-attracting lotion. All you have to do it spread it around on your

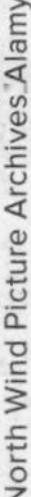

clothes, climb to the top of a mountain, and roll down. By the time you get to the bottom, you'll have enough gold dust stuck to you to live happily ever after.

Joe: That sounds pretty dangerous. And hey, if the lotion makes you rich, why do you have to buy more?

Malcolm: Nah, it don't hurt too bad. And the bottle says that it can take a few tries. But for only ten dollars a bottle, it's worth it. You ought to give it a try.

(Susanna *returns holding a bottle.)*

Susanna: Here we are, Malcolm. Ten dollars.

(Malcolm *reaches into his pocket but, before he can hand over the money,* Lily *storms into the store.)*

Lily: Malcolm Roberts, don't you dare spend my money on your foolishness!

(Malcolm *turns to face her.)*

Malcolm: Aw but Lily, it could make us rich!

Lily: Rich? The only way you'll ever see money is if I earn it with my housework.

Louisa: Can you really earn money by doing housework?

Lily: You'd be surprised how much money a woman can make here. Why, a hardworking woman can make more money in California than most men!

Louisa: What do you mean?

Lily: Well, gold is in short supply. That's what makes it valuable. A woman who knows how to cook, clean, and mend clothes is almost as rare as that gold! She can charge just about as much as she likes.

Joe: Well, Louisa, it looks like you can make money, at least!

Louisa: You're just jealous because I know how to cook, clean, mend clothes, AND mine for gold!

Susanna: Let's get back to business. You're going to need a pan if you're going to mine. I've got one in copper if you're interested.

(Susanna *continues to show her merchandise to* Louisa *and* Joe, *who seem much less interested.)*

Narrator: If Louisa and Joe were like most Forty-niners, they did not strike gold and get rich. Most people who grew wealthy during the Gold Rush made their money by selling supplies, not by finding gold.

Many Forty-niners stayed in California after the Gold Rush ended. They came from so many different places that they gave California a diverse, adventurous, and hard-working population.

Write About It

Write a play about Louisa and Joe two months after their arrival in California. Set the play in Susanna Jones's general store. What do you predict will have happened to Louisa and Joe in two months?

Reference Sources

The Reference Section has a glossary of vocabulary words from the chapters in this book. Use this section to explore new vocabulary as you investigate and take action.

Glossary

A

amendment an addition to the Constitution

article a paragraph in a legal document

assembly a government legislature that represents the people of a particular place

B

bill a suggestion for a new law

blockade an obstacle preventing the movement of people or goods

boundary a line that marks where one area ends and another begins

boycott to refuse to do business or have contact with a person, group, company, country, or product

C

cash crop a plant that is grown for making money

cede to give up something to someone else

charter a document granting someone special legal powers

claim to declare that a place belongs to one's country upon arrival at the place

colony a territory settled by people from another place, usually far away

commerce the buying and selling of goods

composition the way in which something is put together

conquest victory by an invading army

corruption the use of government money for personal gain

covenant a contract, an agreement

currency the type of money used in a particular place

delegate a person who represents other people

demand the level of need for something

dissension disagreement between members of a group over an important issue

diverse containing many types of people or things

E

encomiendas system of forced labor in Spanish colonies

endeavor try hard to achieve a goal

environment the setting in which something takes place

H

habitat an environment that is favorable to the survival of a species

harvest to take and gather such crops as wheat and corn for use

hieroglyph a type of ancient writing that uses pictures for words

hostility opposition; ill will

hunter-gatherer early human who lived by gathering wild plants and hunting animals

I

immigrant a person who arrives in a new country after leaving his or her country of birth

imposing putting in place by a government order

inflation increase in the cost of goods and services

inland in an area that is away from oceans and coastal regions

interchangeable something that can be used in place of something else because it is identical

issue to give out or publish

J

jury a group of citizens that decides the outcome of a court case

L

loom a machine for making thread or yarn into cloth

M

Manifest Destiny the belief that it was divine will for the United States to expand westward to the Pacific Ocean

mercenary soldier from a different country who is paid to fight in a war

merchants people who buy and sell goods

mesa a flat-topped hill with steep sides

militia a group of citizens organized for military service

missionary person on a religious mission, usually to convert others to Christianity

monarch a king or queen who rules a nation

monopoly complete control of something

musket a long gun similar to a rifle

N

navigation the art of guiding a boat, plane, or other transportation vehicle

negotiate to discuss and bargain for a solution

oral history spoken records, including stories, that have been passed from one generation to the next

outpost a fort or other military structure established away from the main army to help guard against surprise attacks

oxen cattle that are used for doing work

physical relating to material objects; having actual form

policy an official position on an issue

potlatch a special feast given by American Indians of the Northwest Coast, in which the guests receive gifts

prairie flat or gently rolling land covered mostly with grasses and wildflowers

press the news media, including newspapers and magazines, websites, and TV and radio

profiteer people who take advantage of a poor economic situation, hoarding goods and selling them at high prices to make a large profit

proprietor the owner

R

reaping having to do with cutting down and gathering

rebel person who defies authority

recession a temporary downturn in business activity

reconcile to become friendly again after a disagreement; to make peace with

reconciliation returning to the previous friendly condition of a relationship after a disagreement

repeal cancelation or withdrawal

republic an area of land that has its own government and elected leaders

resistance defense to diseases developed by the immune system

S

settlement town created by people in an area previously uninhabited by that people

slash-and-burn a method of clearing land for farming by cutting and burning trees

sovereign having independent authority

surge sudden increase

survey to examine and measure

term the period of time during which an elected person is in office

territory an area of land that belongs to a government

totem pole a tall carved log used by American Indians of the Northwest Coast to honor an important person or to mark a special event

traitor someone who betrays his or her country

unconstitutional an action or policy that goes against the Constitution of the United States

vandalism destruction of property

veto to reject or prevent

warship ship mounted with cannons or other large guns

Grade Five

Historical and Social Sciences Content Standards and Analysis Skills

History-Social Sciences Content Standards

United States History and Geography: Making a New Nation

Students in grade five study the development of the nation up to 1850, with an emphasis on the people who were already here, when and from where others arrived, and why they came. Students learn about the colonial government founded on Judeo-Christian principles, the ideals of the Enlightenment, and the English traditions of self-government. They recognize that ours is a nation that has a constitution that derives its power from the people, that has gone through a revolution, that once sanctioned slavery, that experienced conflict over land with the original inhabitants, and that experienced a westward movement that took its people across the continent. Studying the cause, course, and consequences of the early explorations through the War for Independence and western expansion is central to students' fundamental understanding of how the principles of the American republic form the basis of a pluralistic society in which individual rights are secured.

5.1 Students describe the major pre-Columbian settlements, including the cliff dwellers and pueblo people of the desert Southwest, the American Indians of the Pacific Northwest, the nomadic nations of the Great Plains, and the woodland peoples east of the Mississippi River.

1. Describe how geography and climate influenced the way various nations lived and adjusted to the natural environment, including locations of villages, the distinct structures that they built, and how they obtained food, clothing, tools, and utensils.
2. Describe their varied customs and folklore traditions.
3. Explain their varied economies and systems of government.

5.2 Students trace the routes of early explorers and describe the early explorations of the Americas.

1. Describe the entrepreneurial characteristics of early explorers (e.g., Christopher Columbus, Francisco Vásquez de Coronado) and the technological developments that made sea exploration by latitude and longitude possible (e.g., compass, sextant, astrolabe, seaworthy ships, chronometers, gunpowder).
2. Explain the aims, obstacles, and accomplishments of the explorers, sponsors, and leaders of key European expeditions and the reasons Europeans chose to explore and colonize the world (e.g., the Spanish Reconquista, the Protestant Reformation, the Counter Reformation).
3. Trace the routes of the major land explorers of the United States, the distances traveled by explorers, and the Atlantic trade routes that linked Africa, the West Indies, the British colonies, and Europe.
4. Locate on maps of North and South America land claimed by Spain, France, England, Portugal, the Netherlands, Sweden, and Russia.

5.3 Students describe the cooperation and conflict that existed among the American Indians and between the Indian nations and the new settlers.

1. Describe the competition among the English, French, Spanish, Dutch, and Indian nations for control of North America.

2. Describe the cooperation that existed between the colonists and Indians during the 1600s and 1700s (e.g., in agriculture, the fur trade, military alliances, treaties, cultural interchanges).
3. Examine the conflicts before the Revolutionary War (e.g., the Pequot and King Philip's Wars in New England, the Powhatan Wars in Virginia, the French and Indian War).
4. Discuss the role of broken treaties and massacres and the factors that led to the Indians defeat, including the resistance of Indian nations to encroachments and assimilation (e.g., the story of the Trail of Tears).
5. Describe the internecine Indian conflicts, including the competing claims for control of lands (e.g., actions of the Iroquois, Huron, Lakota [Sioux]).
6. Explain the influence and achievements of significant leaders of the time (e.g., John Marshall, Andrew Jackson, Chief Tecumseh, Chief Logan, Chief John Ross, Sequoyah).

5.4 Students understand the political, religious, social, and economic institutions that evolved in the colonial era.

1. Understand the influence of location and physical setting on the founding of the original 13 colonies, and identify on a map the locations of the colonies and of the American Indian nations already inhabiting these areas.
2. Identify the major individuals and groups responsible for the founding of the various colonies and the reasons for their founding (e.g., John Smith, Virginia; Roger Williams, Rhode Island; William Penn, Pennsylvania; Lord Baltimore, Maryland; William Bradford, Plymouth; John Winthrop, Massachusetts).
3. Describe the religious aspects of the earliest colonies (e.g., Puritanism in Massachusetts, Anglicanism in Virginia, Catholicism in Maryland, Quakerism in Pennsylvania).
4. Identify the significance and leaders of the First Great Awakening, which marked a shift in religious ideas, practices, and allegiances in the colonial period, the growth of religious toleration, and free exercise of religion.
5. Understand how the British colonial period created the basis for the development of political self-government and a free-market economic system and the differences between the British, Spanish, and French colonial systems.
6. Describe the introduction of slavery into America, the responses of slave families to their condition, the ongoing struggle between proponents and opponents of slavery, and the gradual institutionalization of slavery in the South.
7. Explain the early democratic ideas and practices that emerged during the colonial period, including the significance of representative assemblies and town meetings.

5.5 Students explain the causes of the American Revolution.

1. Understand how political, religious, and economic ideas and interests brought about the Revolution (e.g., resistance to imperial policy, the Stamp Act, the Townshend Acts, taxes on tea, Coercive Acts).
2. Know the significance of the first and second Continental Congresses and of the Committees of Correspondence.
3. Understand the people and events associated with the drafting and signing of the Declaration of Independence and the document's significance, including the key political concepts it embodies, the origins of those concepts, and its role in severing ties with Great Britain.
4. Describe the views, lives, and impact of key individuals during this period (e.g., King George III, Patrick Henry, Thomas Jefferson, George Washington, Benjamin Franklin, John Adams).

5.6 Students understand the course and consequences of the American Revolution.

1. Identify and map the major military battles, campaigns, and turning points of the Revolutionary War, the roles of the American and British leaders, and the Indian leaders' alliances on both sides.
2. Describe the contributions of France and other nations and of individuals to the outcome of the Revolution (e.g., Benjamin Franklin's negotiations with the French, the French navy, the Treaty of Paris, The Netherlands, Russia, the Marquis Marie Joseph de Lafayette, Tadeusz Ko´sciuszko, Baron Friedrich Wilhelm von Steuben).
3. Identify the different roles women played during the Revolution (e.g., Abigail Adams, Martha Washington, Molly Pitcher, Phillis Wheatley, Mercy Otis Warren).
4. Understand the personal impact and economic hardship of the war on families, problems of financing the war, wartime inflation, and laws against hoarding goods and materials and profiteering.
5. Explain how state constitutions that were established after 1776 embodied the ideals of the American Revolution and helped serve as models for the U.S. Constitution.
6. Demonstrate knowledge of the significance of land policies developed under the Continental Congress (e.g., sale of western lands, the Northwest Ordinance of 1787) and those policies' impact on American Indians' land.
7. Understand how the ideals set forth in the Declaration of Independence changed the way people viewed slavery.

5.7 Students describe the people and events associated with the development of the U.S. Constitution and analyze the Constitution's significance as the foundation of the American republic.

1. List the shortcomings of the Articles of Confederation as set forth by their critics.
2. Explain the significance of the new Constitution of 1787, including the struggles over its ratification and the reasons for the addition of the Bill of Rights.
3. Understand the fundamental principles of American constitutional democracy, including how the government derives its power from the people and the primacy of individual liberty.
4. Understand how the Constitution is designed to secure our liberty by both empowering and limiting central government and compare the powers granted to citizens, Congress, the president, and the Supreme Court with those reserved to the states.
5. Discuss the meaning of the American creed that calls on citizens to safeguard the liberty of individual Americans within a unified nation, to respect the rule of law, and to preserve the Constitution.
6. Know the songs that express American ideals (e.g., "America the Beautiful," "The Star Spangled Banner").

5.8 Students trace the colonization, immigration, and settlement patterns of the American people from 1789 to the mid-1800s, with emphasis on the role of economic incentives, effects of the physical and political geography, and transportation systems.

1. Discuss the waves of immigrants from Europe between 1789 and 1850 and their modes of transportation into the Ohio and Mississippi Valleys and through the Cumberland Gap (e.g., overland wagons, canals, flatboats, steamboats).
2. Name the states and territories that existed in 1850 and identify their locations and major geographical features (e.g., mountain ranges, principal rivers, dominant plant regions).
3. Demonstrate knowledge of the explorations of the trans-Mississippi West following the Louisiana Purchase (e.g., Meriwether Lewis and William Clark, Zebulon Pike, John Fremont).

4. Discuss the experiences of settlers on the overland trails to the West (e.g., location of the routes; purpose of the journeys; the influence of the terrain, rivers, vegetation, and climate; life in the territories at the end of these trails).
5. Describe the continued migration of Mexican settlers into Mexican territories of the West and Southwest.
6. Relate how and when California, Texas, Oregon, and other western lands became part of the United States, including the significance of the Texas War for Independence and the Mexican-American War.

5.9 Students know the location of the current 50 states and the names of their capitals.

Historical and Social Sciences Analysis Skills

In addition to the standards, students demonstrate the following intellectual, reasoning, reflection, and research skills:

Chronological and Spatial Thinking

1. Students place key events and people of the historical era they are studying in a chronological sequence and within a spatial context; they interpret time lines.
2. Students correctly apply terms related to time, including past, present, future, decade, century, and generation.
3. Students explain how the present is connected to the past, identifying both similarities and differences between the two, and how some things change over time and some things stay the same.
4. Students use map and globe skills to determine the absolute locations of places and interpret information available through a map's or globe's legend, scale, and symbolic representations.
5. Students judge the significance of the relative location of a place (e.g., proximity to a harbor, on trade routes) and analyze how relative advantages or disadvantages can change over time.

Research, Evidence, and Point of View

1. Students differentiate between primary and secondary sources.
2. Students pose relevant questions about events they encounter in historical documents, eyewitness accounts, oral histories, letters, diaries, artifacts, photographs, maps, artworks, and architecture.
3. Students distinguish fact from fiction by comparing documentary sources on historical figures and events with fictionalized characters and events.

Historical Interpretation

1. Students summarize the key events of the era they are studying and explain the historical contexts of those events.
2. Students identify the human and physical characteristics of the places they are studying and explain how those features form the unique character of those places.
3. Students identify and interpret the multiple causes and effects of historical events.
4. Students conduct cost-benefit analyses of historical and current events.